P9-DWT-583

ECONOMIC ANALYSIS
FOR BUSINESS DECISIONS

ECONOMIC ANALYSIS FOR BUSINESS DECISIONS

Alan S. Manne

PROFESSOR OF ECONOMICS
GRADUATE SCHOOL OF BUSINESS
STANFORD UNIVERSITY

New York   Toronto   London

McGRAW-HILL BOOK COMPANY   1961

ECONOMIC ANALYSIS FOR BUSINESS DECISIONS

Copyright © 1961 by the McGraw-Hill Book Company, Inc. Printed in the United States of America. All rights reserved. This book, or parts thereof, may not be reproduced in any form without permission of the publishers. *Library of Congress Catalog Card Number* 61-11130

4 5 6 7 – M P – 9 8

38820

PREFACE

The traditional meeting place of the economic analyst and the business executive has been a battleground: the Congressional hearing, the courtroom, or the debate platform. It is a comparatively recent phenomenon for members of each group to infiltrate into the jobs of the other and for both parties to find profit in the interchange of ideas.

When it comes to matters of public policy within a market economy—taxation, foreign trade, antitrust, or labor relations—there still remains a wide gulf between the views of most economists and those of most business executives. But when it comes to analysis of internal operations of the business enterprise, the ideological barriers seem to have crumbled away and a fruitful area has opened up, an area sometimes known as "engineering economics" or "operations research" or "management science."

This volume is intended as a survey and an introduction to the new and rapidly changing area that lies between the disciplines of economics and those of industrial administration. I have tried to concentrate on those topics possessing an essential unity with each other and with the traditional subject matter of microeconomics: the logic of choice. Four chapters deal with linear programming, two with integer programming, and three with inventory models and sequential decision theory. Considerable stress is placed on the idea of sensitivity analysis and on the role played by implicit prices in such analyses.

After much deliberation, I have refrained from including certain related topics: demand forecasting, statistical cost functions, queuing theory, computer simulation, portfolio selection, and oligopoly. Each of these items would require more knowledge of probability theory or numerical analysis or economics than is presupposed for the other portions of this volume. From my own experience, I should guess that most instructors—depending upon the background of their students—will wish to combine one or more of these related topics with the main body of subject matter provided here. A set of references for this purpose is included.

The material has evolved out of notes and problems utilized in a first-year graduate course, one offered jointly since 1957 by the department of economics and the department of industrial administration at Yale. Some topics have also been tested successfully on third-year undergraduates in an economic theory seminar. Most of my students have had limited backgrounds in mathematics, and the course has been designed around this fact. I hope that I have not offended too many of my colleagues by sacrificing rigor in the interests of intuitive appeal and of readability.

There is no getting around the fact that this text presumes some minimum amount of preparation in both economics and mathematics. The necessary economics background consists of familiarity with such homely but essential distinctions as those between fixed and variable costs, between present and future cash outlays, between sunk costs and uncommitted costs, and, above all, the distinction between an economic model and the underlying empirical reality. Such a background might be provided either by an undergraduate course featuring some such text as Grant and Ireson's *Engineering Economy* or, alternatively, by an undergraduate course emphasizing public policy and utilizing, say, Samuelson's *Economics: An Introductory Analysis*.

As far as mathematics is concerned, the first seven chapters require nothing more advanced than high school algebra. If the reader really knows what it means to solve a set of simultaneous linear equations, he should have no difficulty with linear or integer programming—provided that he is faithful in working through the exercises at the end of each chapter. The use of matrix notation is confined to a single footnote. Certain specialized points arising in Chapters 4 and 5 are relegated to Appendixes. The last three chapters, dealing with inventory models and with sequential decisions, require somewhat more in the way of background. These chapters presuppose that the reader has been introduced to the elementary notions of probability: a random variable, a probability distribution, and a mean. In addition, there are portions of Chapter 8 that make use of the differential calculus.

It is a pleasure to acknowledge indebtedness to all my former students and especially to John Colley, Cornelius Day, T. N. Srinivasan, and Emmanuel Uren. Through his painstaking review, Mr. Srinivasan, now a colleague at the Cowles Foundation, has inspired a large number of improvements in this manuscript.

Ralph Gomory has been most helpful in criticizing the chapters on integer programming; Jacob Marschak and Herbert Scarf have reviewed those on inventory theory. I am grateful to the IBM Research Center, Yorktown Heights, New York, for financial support during the writing of several chapters. My indebtedness to other present and former colleagues, George Dantzig, Tjalling Koopmans, and Harry Markowitz, will, I hope, appear obvious.

Judith Schiff has done a nice job of typing from a battered manuscript. My wife and children have been admirable in providing both toleration and inspiration.

Alan S. Manne

A disclaimer: All company names employed here refer to purely fictitious organizations.

CONTENTS

CHAPTER ONE

INTRODUCTION

The phrase "economic analysis for business decisions" brings to mind a number of stereotyped pictures of analysts: first, perhaps, the type of person who persists in forecasting general business conditions, despite repeated evidence that his forecasts are slightly less reliable than flipping a coin. Second, there is the notion of an efficiency expert, an unpleasant man with a stop watch who spends his time telling other people how to make their work easier. (Turn the lights up, and worker productivity increases. Turn them down, and it goes up some more.) A slight variant upon this is the kind of man who is hired specifically in order to rediscover reforms which are widely known to be long overdue but which have been blocked by the intransigence of a superannuated vice-president. Still another notion is that an economist is a staff man who at rare intervals comes upon glaringly obvious oversights and then tells his chief how to make money by correcting them.

The term "economic analysis" may have overtones of all these things, but it is not adequately defined by any one of them. Perhaps the last comes closest to the point. By nature, an economist *is* a staff man, a specialist who makes recommendations, but who does not have the final say-so on policy matters. It is also true that this kind of specialist is concerned with finding ways to increase the organization's profitability. (Institutional advertisements to the contrary notwithstanding, most firms really are in business to make money.)

There are, however, at least two serious objections to defining an economist as one who goes about finding obvious ways to improve things. First is the adjective "obvious," and second the ambiguity of what is meant by "improving" things. On the first of these points, it must be admitted that there often are clear-cut ways for money to be saved. Examples: (1) hauling steel from Pittsburgh to Chicago at the same time that steel of a comparable size and quality is moving in the opposite direction and (2) devoting more individual sales effort to small customers than to large ones. Whenever instances of this sort come to his attention, the analyst is lucky indeed. About all that he needs to do in order to justify his pay check is to convince other people that the current operation is really as inefficient as he believes it to be.

In most well-run organizations, he can seldom expect to be this fortunate. If he is able to improve the operation at all, it is likely to be by some means that is quite roundabout. In the steel-shipping example just discussed, what he will observe much more frequently is that some structural shapes are moving from Pittsburgh to, say, Indianapolis, at the same time as sheets are going from Chicago to Detroit (Figure 1-1). In this case, before he pronounces adversely upon the current way of coordinating shipments, he will have to make a fairly careful study of the product capacities in both mill areas and also of the relative costs of hauling steel by rail, truck, and water over all four possible routes: (a) Pittsburgh-Indianapolis, (b) Pittsburgh-Detroit, (c) Chicago-Indianapolis, and (d) Chicago-Detroit. If the economist is to demonstrate that it pays to alter the current transportation arrangements, what he must show is that the *combined* cost of manufacturing and shipping over routes (a) and (d) exceeds the combined cost over (b) and (c).

This single example brings out the essence of rational economic planning with which we shall be concerned: pinpointing the unfavorable as well as the favorable consequences of each course of action that is open to the organization and then finding a suitable criterion for choice among these alternatives. Economic analysis, as employed here, is largely an extension of formal logic—the logic of choice. If nothing else, this volume should convince the reader that economic alternatives exist and that occasionally it is even possible to find rational grounds for preferring one alternative to another.

Fig. 1-1. Four traffic routing possibilities.

Not all economic choices are difficult ones to make. When steel is being hauled in both directions between Pittsburgh and Chicago, very little mental effort is needed in order to decide that a cost-saving improvement is possible. When four cities are involved, the back of an envelope will suffice for any economic calculations. And when, as in more realistic situations, upwards of a dozen areas are involved, the easiest procedure may be to apply the idea that has come to be called "linear programming."[1]

The early chapters of this volume (Chapters 2 to 5) are concerned with linear programming and with the range of applications of its use. Next come Chapters 6 and 7 on integer programming, the analysis of indivisibilities and of either-or choices. All this earlier material is based upon deterministic assumptions, replacing, if necessary, a probability distribution by a single-valued "best estimate." The later chapters, however, are explicitly concerned with cases in which randomness and uncertainty play a crucial role. In the theory of inventory stockage, for example, it makes no sense to talk about a "safety stock" without recognizing the random nature of demand. Chapters 8 to 10 make use of a variety of mathematical techniques, but there is nevertheless an underlying unity with the earlier material, even aside from the fact that linear programming can be employed to analyze certain types of random sequential decision processes. The logic of making optimal economic decisions remains fundamentally the same whether the problem under study is selection of a product mix, production smoothing over time, inventory stockage, equipment investment, or the allocation of funds to research and development.

Whether these decisions are obvious or not so obvious, the logic of choice remains much the same, and so do the difficulties. The difficulties typically stem from the ambiguity of what is meant by an improvement—the fact that it is next to impossible

---

[1] Priority for the invention of linear programming belongs to a Soviet mathematician, L. Kantorovich. An English translation of his 1939 paper, "Mathematical Methods of Organizing and Planning Production," appears in *Management Science*, July, 1960. Kantorovich's work was neglected both in his own county and in the outside world for many years. Meanwhile, in 1947, George B. Dantzig, a United States Air Force analyst, independently came upon similar ideas. Dantzig is credited with having devised the general-purpose technique of solution known as the "simplex method." His fundamental paper is entitled "Maximization of a Linear Function of Variables Subject to Linear Inequalities" and appears in T. C. Koopmans (ed.), *Activity Analysis of Production and Allocation*, John Wiley & Sons, Inc., New York, 1951, chap. 21.

to relate all the diverse goals of a modern corporation to one another through the common denominator of dollar profits. True, it is often possible to observe that the company will save money by shutting down an antiquated production facility. But it is also true that a shutdown will ordinarily damage the local good will that has taken years to build up. The shutdown, moreover, is almost sure to be resisted by the company-wide union. In such a case as this, the role of the economist is not to square the circle. Immediate dollar cost considerations alone will not dictate what policy ought to be followed. Rather, the economist's job is to make meaningful estimates of the full "opportunity costs" implied by the no-shutdown policy. Such a choice is seldom a simple one of either closing down or maintaining the *status quo*. At the very least, one would want to explore such alternatives as modernization or replacing one of the product lines with another.

The economist's contribution, then, lies in *imaginatively* defining the range of choices open to the company, narrowing the range as far as possible, and indicating clearly the extent of incompatibility between the company's individual aims. His is the quiet, logical voice insisting that the enterprise cannot simultaneously pay maximum wages to its employees and operate at the lowest cost. It cannot sell the highest-quality product to its customers and also charge the lowest prices. It cannot at the same time pay out maximum dividends to its stockholders and grow at the fastest rate. When science and technology progress to the point at which all these things are simultaneously compatible, there will no longer be any business decisions for economists to analyze.

CHAPTER TWO

THE FUNDAMENTALS
OF RESOURCE ALLOCATION

Capital budgeting

Perhaps the best way to understand what is involved in problems of economic choice is to start with a highly simplified model of what is ordinarily the most important of all corporate decisions—drawing up an investment budget. Typically, such a budget applies to a forthcoming calendar year, but it may refer to a two- or even a five-year period. Logically, the first step in this process consists of a forecast of the funds that will be available from internal sources of finance—primarily depreciation reserves and retained earnings. Suppose that this forecast works out as follows:

Retained earnings	$20 million
Depreciation reserves	10 million
Total funds available from internal sources	$30 million

The next step consists of a survey of investment opportunities among department heads and plant managers. For our purposes, we shall assume that there is only one criterion relevant to the problem of investment choice: expected dollar return on investment. In this crude model, we shall neglect the very real problem of evaluating riskiness and also of placing a dollar value upon investments in such intangibles as product development, employee morale, and community relations. The investment opportunities under survey will be presumed comparable in all respects, except the factor of percentage rate of return on investment. We can suppose that the results of our survey are as follows:

Per cent return on investment, per annum	Number of dollars' worth of projects, millions	Cumulative dollars' worth, millions
30	8	8
25	12	20
20	15	35
15	10	45

It is now an easy matter to see how the $30 million available from internal sources should be allocated among the different projects so as to maximize the total return. All those yielding 25 per cent or more should be undertaken. Those yielding 15 per cent or less should be eliminated. And of those yielding exactly 20 per cent, just $10 million worth should be initiated. The "cutoff rate of return," or "implicit worth of capital," in this case is said to be 20 per cent per annum. Another way to put this is to say that if just $30 million worth of funds were available, it would be possible to utilize as much as an additional $5 million before the incremental yield dropped below 20 per cent.

Once this calculation has been performed, a number of interesting by-products emerge. For one thing, suppose that a new project, one not included in the original survey, is brought up for consideration, and suppose that the rate of return on this is only 13 per cent. Clearly enough, since this return lies below the cutoff rate, the project can be dismissed from further consideration, assuming always that the rate of return is a suitable basis for ranking projects. Conversely, if a new 25 per cent project arises, it will pay to undertake it, obtaining the funds by reducing the volume of investment planned at the 20 per cent cutoff, or implicit, rate of return.

Possibly the most important use of the cutoff rate concept lies in raising questions about the adequacy of the internal financing that is available. As soon as it is apparent that the incremental, or "marginal," worth of capital is 20 per cent, it is quite likely that the financial officers will be stimulated into thinking about ways of supplementing the existing sources of funds, e.g., to retain a larger share of earnings in the form of undistributed profits, or to draw down the investment in inventory, or to float new securities, or . . . . The implicit rate of return provides a means for comparing the efficacy of each of these alternatives.[1]

A product-mix choice

In ranking investment alternatives as was just done above, the arithmetic was made easy by one notable feature of the problem: the fundamental resource limitations were of a single kind, a shortage of investment capital. The allocation job consisted simply of distributing this shortage among the alternative money-making projects in the least harmful way. But what if more than one bottleneck is operative? What if several different kinds of resources are in short supply? Our next example is concerned with a problem of this sort—an example which will first be solved by graphical means and then by linear programming.

Consider a brass mill whose output is limited by two bottleneck operations—its extrusion press and its annealing capacity. Management's problem is one of utilizing the existing facilities in the most profitable manner and only indirectly one of determining whether the enterprise ought to expand or to contract its investment in these facilities.

The rods and tubes that can be made by this mill may be grouped into four general types—for short, here labeled A, B, C, and D. The over-all decision confronting the mill is that of

[1] For more on this subject, see Joel Dean, *Capital Budgeting*, Columbia University Press, New York, 1951.

determining how large the monthly production ought to be within each of these four classes.

The mill is a small enough factor in the market so that it can plan to sell as much or as little of each product as it pleases without appreciably affecting either the current price or its future selling opportunities for any of these items. The unit sales realization on product A, for example, is $.50 per pound regardless of the total number of pounds sold.

The mill's costs are segregated into two kinds: incremental costs which are proportional to output and overhead items which are independent of output. Given the stipulation that the mill's equipment is not to be altered, it is entirely proper to ignore the overhead costs in deciding upon the most desirable product mix. Since these fixed costs cannot be affected by a product-mix decision, it would be quite meaningless to attempt to spread out such costs over individual products. Overhead items would include local property taxes on the plant, interest and depreciation charges, and the bulk of executive compensation. Incremental, or marginal, costs, on the other hand, are those which can be reduced as output drops off and increased as it picks up, e.g., materials, unskilled labor, and electric power. If it turns out that the incremental costs attributable to product A are $.34 per pound, then we have the "unit payoff," or "contribution to profit and overhead," for the one item:

Unit sales realization $-$ incremental cost $=$ unit payoff
$$\$.50 \qquad - \qquad \$.34 \qquad = \$.16 \text{ per pound}$$

At this point, knowing the incremental payoff per pound of output, we can conveniently shift from physical units of output (pounds) to economic ones (dollars). In all subsequent calculations, instead of talking in terms of a single pound's worth of product A ($.16 worth of payoff), we shall employ a unit of 6,250 pounds' worth of this product, that is, an output just sufficient to result in a $1,000 contribution to profit and overhead. The reader can verify that this change of scale does no more to change the nature of the brass mill's problem than would a change in units of measurement from pounds to tons.

Having estimated the unit payoff from each of the four products and having made the appropriate conversion from physical units into a uniform economic one ($1,000 worth of payoff), we can state the input requirements of bottleneck equipment in these same terms:

Input requirements	Product class			
	A	B	C	D
Extrusion press time (hours required per $1,000 contribution to profit and overhead)...........	4.0	2.0	1.5	3.5
Annealing capacity time (hours required per $1,000 contribution to profit and overhead)...........	0	1.5	3.0	1.0

Utilizing this information, we now make a cross plot of the extrusion press time versus the annealing time on each product required in order to yield a stipulated amount of payoff, for example, $100,000 per month (see points A, B, C, and D in Figure 2-1). On the basis of this diagram alone, we cannot give any definite answers to the question of which items ought to be produced, but we can at least rule out one of the possibilities, namely, product D.

Why can this item be discarded from further consideration? Consider a point like F on the line segment AB. Note that any point along the segment AB corresponds to a monthly payoff of $100,000. Point F, for example, represents the option of producing $33,333 worth of payoff through product A and $66,667 worth through product B.* Now in order to produce $100,000 by means of this combination of products A and B, we need the same amount of annealing capacity as for $100,000 worth of D, but much less extrusion press time is required. By the same kind of reasoning, point E corresponds to a different combination of items A and B, but one which still yields just

* $33,333 = (FB/AB)$100,000. And similarly,

$$\$66,667 = \left(\frac{AF}{AB}\right)\$100,000.$$

$100,000 and which uses less annealing capacity than D. In fact, by operating at any point along the line segment EF, it will be possible to produce the same payoff as that which corresponds to point D and to use less of both bottleneck resources.

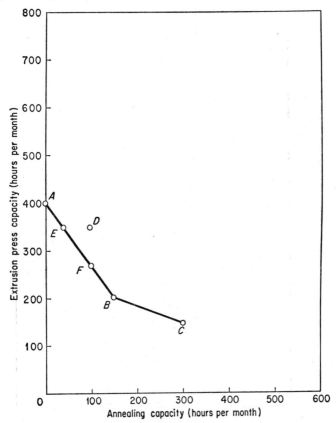

Fig. 2-1. Brass mill problem: inputs required for monthly payoff of $100 thousand.

Clearly, item D is an inefficient way to make money. It will always be better to produce either A or B or some combination of the two. This still leaves unresolved the question of whether or not A and B should be produced in preference to C.

Having ruled out product D, we are now ready to proceed with
the main line of analysis—taking into account the limitations
both upon extrusion press time and on annealing capacity. If
we are told that these two limits are, respectively, 275 and 300

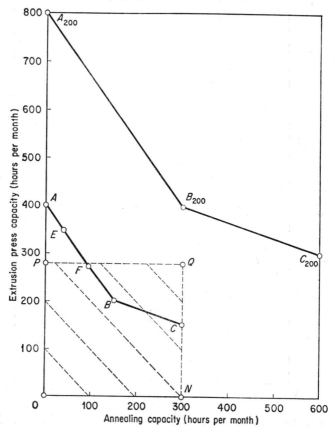

Fig. 2-2. Brass mill problem: effect of capacity limitations.

hours per month, and if we plot them on Figure 2-2, one thing
about the ultimate product mix becomes apparent. No matter
what combination of products A, B, and C is produced, the only
feasible solutions will be those lying within the crosshatched

rectangle $NOPQ$. All points that lie outside this rectangle would violate one or both of the capacity restraints. From this diagram, it is possible to see that the zero-output point 0 is a feasible one, as are the points F, B, and C that lie along the \$100,000 iso-payoff line.[1] Points A and E, however, lie outside the area of feasibility, even though they too are on the \$100,000 contour line. Furthermore, all points on the \$200,000 line, $A_{200}B_{200}C_{200}$, lie outside the feasible region. Figure 2-2, then, provides us with a further narrowing down of the possibilities. It says that, no matter what solution is finally adopted, the process of choice certainly need not lead to a payoff below \$100,000 per month, nor can it bring about one that exceeds \$200,000. The optimal solution lies somewhere between these limits.

Figure 2-3 indicates the final solution to this one problem, namely, point Q with a \$150,000 contribution to profit and overhead. The outputs of both products A and D are zero. Those of B and C are as follows:

$$\text{Output of } B = \$150,000 \ \frac{QC_{150}}{B_{150}C_{150}} = \$100,000 \text{ per month}$$

$$\text{Output of } C = \$150,000 \ \frac{QB_{150}}{B_{150}C_{150}} = \$ 50,000 \text{ per month}$$

Once known, the answer to this problem is painfully obvious. The necessary solution is one in which both bottleneck facilities are fully employed and one in which just two products are produced in positive amounts. After the items to be produced are identified, the rest is just a matter of solving simultaneous equations for the outputs. Denoting by x_2 and x_3, respectively, the output of items B and C, we obtain the final answer through solving the system:

$$2.0x_2 + 1.5x_3 = 275 \text{ hours of extrusion press time} \quad (2\text{-}1)$$
$$1.5x_2 + 3.0x_3 = 300 \text{ hours of annealing capacity} \quad (2\text{-}2)$$

---

[1] The line ABC is said to be a \$100,000 iso-payoff line in the sense that all output points along this line correspond to the *same* payoff: \$100,000 per month. Similarly the line $A_{200}B_{200}C_{200}$ represents a \$200,000 iso-payoff line. Note the similarity between this scheme of representation and that of weather map making, where it is customary to plot isobars, lines of equal barometric pressure.

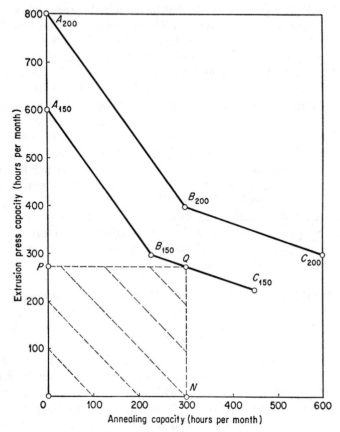

Fig. 2-3. Brass mill problem: optimal solution.

Following these through, we find that our algebraic results check with those previously obtained by graphical means:

Output of $B = x_2 = 100$ thousand dollars per month
Output of $C = x_3 = 50$ thousand dollars per month

We could just as well have put our brass mill product-mix problem into algebraic form and set it up as a linear programming model:

Maximize the payoff =
$$\$1{,}000x_1 + \$1{,}000x_2 + \$1{,}000x_3 + \$1{,}000x_4 \quad \text{(2-3)}$$

subject to the conditions:

$$4.0x_1 + 2.0x_2 + 1.5x_3 + 3.5x_4 = 275 \qquad \text{(2-4)}$$
$$0x_1 + 1.5x_2 + 3.0x_3 + 1.0x_4 = 300 \qquad \text{(2-5)}$$

and $\qquad\qquad x_1,\ x_2,\ x_3,\ x_4 \geq 0$ (2-6)

Solving a system of simultaneous equations like (2-1) and (2-2) is not a very difficult job. It is just a matter of finding two unknowns which satisfy the two conditions. In the case of the linear programming equations (2-4) and (2-5), however, there are four unknowns: the quantity of output of each of the four products A, B, C, and D. Many values of x_1, x_2, x_3, and x_4 can be found which satisfy these two equations and also the non-negativity conditions (2-6).[1] But we are concerned with more than just finding a feasible solution—one which stays within the equipment time availabilities. We want to find the most profitable one among those that are feasible. In algebraic language, we are looking for values of x_1, x_2, x_3, and x_4 that will maximize the payoff expression (2-3) subject to conditions (2-4), (2-5), and (2-6). It is in order to locate this maximum that the concept of implicit values is so important in linear programming. Even in the absence of a diagram like Figure 2-3, implicit values furnish the signal that will tell us which of the four items should be left alone and which two should be produced. Once we know the items to be produced, the rest is easy—just a matter of solving simultaneous equations like (2-1) and (2-2).

Implicit values

An implicit value in our brass mill problem is defined in much the same way as in the capital budgeting case. It serves to measure the increase in the amount of payoff obtained per unit increase in the availability of a limiting factor. In the capital

---

[1] A mathematician is very literal-minded. He will insist upon a black-and-white statement that he is not permitted to produce negative quantities of output and thereby convert physical products back into equipment time!

budgeting case, investment capital was the fundamental limit. The implicit value, or cutoff rate of return, measured the increase in annual dollar return associated with a \$1 increase in the availability of investment capital. With \$30 million of capital available, this incremental worth came to 20 per cent per annum.

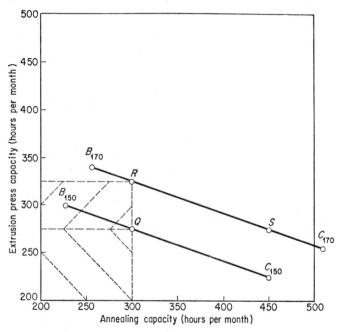

Fig. 2-4. Brass mill problem: implicit price calculation.

In the brass mill problem, there are two kinds of capacity limits—extrusion press time and annealing time—and consequently two implicit values to be measured.[1] If we wish, these values can be calculated geometrically from Figure 2-4, an enlarged portion of the original diagram. Holding the annealing capacity constant at 300 hours per month and increasing the

[1] Among the many synonyms for "implicit value" are "incremental" and "intrinsic" value; also "dual variables," "Lagrangian multipliers," "shadow prices," "internal prices," and "efficiency prices."

extrusion press time by 50 hours, from 275 to 325, the optimum is shifted from point Q on the \$150,000 iso-payoff line to point R on the \$170,000 line. The implicit worth of extrusion press time, indicated by the symbol u_1, is therefore

$$u_1 = \frac{\$170,000 - \$150,000 \text{ per month}}{325 - 275 \text{ hours per month}}$$
$$= \$400 \text{ per extrusion press hour}$$

Note that the change in extrusion capacity brings about a change in the amounts produced of *both* item B and item C. The output of B increases from a value of \$100,000 to \$140,000 per month. That of item C decreases from \$50,000 to \$30,000. The over-all effect is an increase of \$20,000 in the contribution to profit and overhead.[1]

The incremental value of annealing capacity can be determined in a similar way: Hold the extrusion press time at its original level of 275 hours and increase the annealing capacity from 300 to 450 hours. The optimal solution now lies at point S along the \$170,000 iso-payoff line. At point S, the outputs of B and C yield, respectively, \$40,000 and \$130,000. And the incremental value of annealing capacity, u_2, can be measured by taking the ratio of the change in payoff to the change in capacity:[2]

$$u_2 = \frac{\$170,000 - \$150,000 \text{ per month}}{450 - 300 \text{ hours per month}}$$
$$= \$133 \text{ per hour of annealing capacity}$$

[1] The reader should verify for himself that

$$x_2 = \$170,000 \, \frac{RC_{170}}{B_{170}C_{170}} = \$140,000$$

$$x_3 = \$170,000 \, \frac{RB_{170}}{B_{170}C_{170}} = \$30,000$$

[2] In calculating both u_1 and u_2, we can assign any convenient magnitude to the increment in capacity provided that the altered product mix still contains positive quantities of both item B and item C. Subject to this proviso, the size of the change may be selected arbitrarily, for the *ratio* of the change in payoff to the change in capacity will remain constant. In the case of u_2, for example, it would have been equally satisfactory to work with a denominator of 10 hours or of 200 hours instead of the 150 hours actually shown.

Having measured the implicit worth of the two kinds of capacity ($400 and $133 per hour), we are now in a position to put this knowledge to use in checking the optimality of the solution represented by point Q. Let z_1 represent the opportunity cost, or incremental value, of the equipment that is needed in order to produce $1,000 worth of output of item A. Then

$$z_1 = 4.0u_1 + 0u_2 \quad = \$1,600 \text{ per unit of item } A \quad (2\text{-}7)$$

Similarly,

$$z_2 = 2.0u_1 + 1.5u_2 = \$1,000 \text{ per unit of item } B \quad (2\text{-}8)$$
$$z_3 = 1.5u_1 + 3.0u_2 = \$1,000 \text{ per unit of item } C \quad (2\text{-}9)$$
$$z_4 = 3.5u_1 + 1.0u_2 = \$1,533 \text{ per unit of item } D \quad (2\text{-}10)$$

These definitions of $z_1, \ldots, z_4$ lead to a rather remarkable result. Both z_2 and z_3 are identical with the payoff from one unit of product. That is to say, the incremental worth of the equipment absorbed in producing one unit of items B and C exactly offsets the incremental payoff received from these items. On the other hand, z_1 and z_4, the incremental value of the facilities needed for producing A and D, both exceed the unit payoff. This example underscores the signaling purpose served by the implicit prices, u_1 and u_2. A knowledge of these quantities enables us to choose which pair of products ought to be produced and which should not.

Equally well, equations (2-8) and (2-9) can be put into reverse. If we have a tentative solution to our problem, and this solution is one in which items B and C are being produced, then we know how large z_2 and z_3 have to be: just large enough to equal the unit payoff, $1,000. Here, instead of regarding z_2 and z_3 as the unknowns, we are perfectly justified in regarding *them* as given and in solving (2-8) and (2-9) simultaneously for the unknowns u_1 and u_2. The resulting values will be identical with those obtained graphically. Should the calculations reveal that z_1 and z_4 (the opportunity costs, respectively, of items A and D) exceed the unit payoffs of $1,000, the tentative solution cannot be improved upon. It is an optimal one. If, on the other hand, z_1 lies below the $1,000 unit payoff, things will be improved by producing item A and by eliminating the output of either B or C. This trial-and-error procedure—picking a pair of products, calculating implicit prices and opportunity costs, and shifting, if necessary, to another pair of products—is what is known technically as the simplex procedure for obtaining numerical solutions to linear programming problems. In subsequent chapters, we shall sketch out this method more precisely and show how it can be applied to a much wider range of problems of economic choice than the brass mill product-mix case just studied.

At the heart of this formidable-looking procedure, though, lies a simple idea—the concept of implicit prices. It is possible to look at these quantities from two viewpoints: that of numerical calculation and that of economic analysis. From the viewpoint of numerical calculation, these prices are simply defined as the value that has to be assigned to each of the bottleneck resources so that if a product is produced, the total value of the resources absorbed in producing that item will just equal the unit payoff. From the viewpoint of economic analysis, however, these prices have a somewhat deeper meaning. They measure the incremental worth of the bottleneck factors. In our capital budgeting problem, the incremental worth of capital turned out to be 20 per cent per annum. In the product-mix problem, the figures turned out to be $400 per hour for extrusion press time and $133 per hour for annealing capacity. Just as an implicit rate of return of 20 per cent per annum on capital is likely to start a financial officer thinking of possible ways to increase the amount of investment funds available, so a figure of $400 per hour is quite likely to make an industrial engineer start thinking of ways to break the extrusion press bottleneck—perhaps by overtime, perhaps by modernization, or perhaps by some other means.

In all likelihood, the most important thing to be derived from the linear programming calculation is not the optimal product mix itself, but rather the implicit values of the individual bottlenecks. This seems typical of problems of economic choice. We are interested in finding optimal solutions to a problem under carefully defined given conditions—precisely so that we can find out what it would be worth to us if those conditions could themselves be altered.

EXERCISES

Note: The reader should not proceed to Chapter 3 until he has worked these problems.

2-1. What changes, if any, would occur in the optimal solution of the brass mill production problem as a result of a uniform 25 per cent increase in the profitability of each of the four items? What would result from a uniform 50 per cent drop? Can you generalize your conclusions?

2-2. Suppose that the annealing capacity is held constant at 300 hours per month. How low would the extrusion press capacity have to drop before it paid to concentrate production exclusively on item C? How high would it have to rise before it became desirable to produce any of item A? Beyond this last point, what would be the implicit value of extrusion capacity? Of annealing capacity?

2-3. A precision-parts manufacturer's output is limited by the capacity of his 9 jig borers and 12 automatic-screw machines. He can count on 35 hours per week of productive time on each of these 21 units. His products may be grouped into five classes depending upon both the size and the precision requirements of the item. The machining requirements and unit payoffs on each are:

	Part class number				
	1	2	3	4	5
Jig-borer hours per thousand pieces........	8	9	15	6	10
Screw-machine hours per thousand pieces...	8	15	12	16	5
Contribution to profit and overhead per thousand pieces......................	$10	$15	$20	$15	$10

What is the most profitable product mix for this manufacturer, and what is the implicit worth of machine time? By how much would the $10 unit payoff have to increase on part 1 before it became profitable to include any of it in the product mix? By how much further would the payoff on this part have to increase before it paid to concentrate the shop's entire capacity on the one item? What then would be the implicit worth of jig-borer and of screw-machine time?

2-4. A fertilizer manufacturer wants to produce a product with a minimum nitrogen content of 5 pounds *per bag* and a minimum phosphate content of 10 pounds *per bag*. (For purposes of this example, you may assume that there is no effective restriction upon the total weight of the individual bags.) Four ingredients are available:

	Ingredient			
	A	*B*	*C*	*D*
Cost, dollars per 100 pounds............	$1.00	$2.00	$1.50	$2.00
Nitrogen content per 100 pounds........	5	12	2	8
Phosphate content per 100 pounds......	6	5	12	10

What will be the minimum-cost blend of ingredients? How much will a bag of this product weigh? What is the implicit cost of satisfying the nitrogen requirement? The phosphate requirement?

CHAPTER THREE

ON SOLVING LINEAR PROGRAMMING PROBLEMS

Some definitions

As an instrument of economic logic, linear programming has been applied to a wide variety of problems ranging from product-mix decisions to inventory control and equipment selection. In view of this diversity of uses, it is not at all easy to draw a sharp line of demarcation between those applications that are amenable to linear programming and those that are not. In purely mathematical terms, though, linear programming is not at all difficult to define. It is simply a matter of assigning values to n individual unknowns $x_1, x_2, \ldots, x_j, \ldots, x_n$ in such a way as to:

Maximize total payoff =
$$p_1x_1 + p_2x_2 + \cdots + p_jx_j + \cdots + p_nx_n \quad (3\text{-}1)$$

subject to the conditions:

$$a_{11}x_1 + a_{12}x_2 + \cdots + a_{1j}x_j + \cdots + a_{1n}x_n = q_1$$
$$a_{21}x_1 + a_{22}x_2 + \cdots + a_{2j}x_j + \cdots + a_{2n}x_n = q_2 \quad (3\text{-}2)$$

$$a_{i1}x_1 + a_{i2}x_2 + \cdots + a_{ij}x_j + \cdots + a_{in}x_n = q_i$$

$$\qquad \qquad \cdot \quad \cdot \qquad (3\text{-}2)$$
$$\qquad \qquad \cdot \qquad \cdot \quad \textit{Cont.}$$

$$a_{m1}x_1 + a_{m2}x_2 + \cdots + a_{mj}x_j + \cdots + a_{mn}x_n = q_m$$

and $\qquad\qquad x_1, x_2, \ldots, x_j, \ldots, x_n \geq 0 \qquad\qquad (3\text{-}3)$

It is understood all along that the symbols p_j, a_{ij}, and q_i are parameters; i.e., they represent quantities that are to be specified in advance. Ordinarily, the term "payoff coefficient" is attached to the n quantities p_j; "input-output coefficient" to the $m \cdot n$ terms a_{ij}; and "right-hand-side constant" to the m individual q_i. More compactly, the conditions above may be written:

Maximize $\qquad\qquad \displaystyle\sum_{j=1}^{n} p_j x_j \qquad\qquad (3\text{-}1a)$

subject to the conditions:

$$\sum_{j=1}^{n} a_{ij}x_j = q_i \qquad (i = 1, \ldots, m) \qquad (3\text{-}2a)$$

and $\qquad\qquad x_j \geq 0 \qquad (j = 1, \ldots, n) \qquad (3\text{-}3a)$

Despite the forbidding appearance of conditions (3-1) to (3-3), it is easy enough to give a direct interpretation of the brass mill product-mix problem in this same format. Rewriting the equations from the preceding chapter for ready reference here, we have:

Maximize the payoff =
$$\$1,000x_1 + \$1,000x_2 + \$1,000x_3 + \$1,000x_4 \quad (2\text{-}3)$$

subject to the conditions:

$$4.0x_1 + 2.0x_2 + 1.5x_3 + 3.5x_4 = 275 \qquad (2\text{-}4)$$
$$0x_1 + 1.5x_2 + 3.0x_3 + 1.0x_4 = 300 \qquad (2\text{-}5)$$
and $\qquad\qquad x_1, x_2, x_3, x_4 \geq 0 \qquad (2\text{-}6)$

The payoff expression (2-3) in the brass mill problem corresponds to the one written in more general notation as (3-1) above. Equations (2-4) and (2-5) correspond to the input-output conditions (3-2). And (2-6) is identical with the nonnegativity restrictions (3-3).

The number of x_j unknowns, n, in the numerical example is equal to four—one unknown for the quantity of each of the four mill products. The number of input-output equations, m, is two —one for each of the two capacity limitations q_1 and q_2, 275 and 300 hours respectively. Altogether, there are $m \cdot n$ input-output coefficients a_{ij}—4.0 hours of extrusion press time per \$1,000 worth of product A; 2.0 hours per \$1,000 worth of product B; and so on. Finally, there are the four payoff coefficients p_j—here of a quite special sort—\$1,000 each. Note that, in general, there is no need for either the p_j or the a_{ij} to be positive in sign. A negative payoff coefficient could refer to a cost rather than to a profit item.[1] A negative input-output coefficient could correspond to an output rather than to an input as here. For computational uniformity, we shall make one specific restriction as to the sign of the parameters. All the q_i will be assumed to be either positive or zero.[2]

The simplex method

With these preliminaries out of the way, we are ready to proceed with a numerical example of the simplex technique for linear programming calculations. Recall from our previous discussion that each step of this procedure consists of picking a pair of products to be produced, calculating implicit prices and

---

[1] A cost-minimization problem may always be converted into a profit-maximization problem by multiplying each of the original payoff coefficients by -1.

[2] Even though the "natural" way to formulate an economic problem might involve negative values for some of the q_i, there is an easy way to circumvent this difficulty. Just multiply the entire equation through by -1. If, say, we desire values of the unknowns x_j such that

$$2x_1 - 3x_2 = -6$$

the following condition is fully equivalent:

$$-2x_1 + 3x_2 = 6$$

opportunity costs, and then shifting, if necessary, to another pair of products. This is essentially all that is involved, whether the procedure is carried out by hand or by means of an electronic calculator.

Now suppose that, instead of having had the foresight to assign zero values to the unknowns x_1 and x_4 and using equations (2-4) and (2-5) to evaluate x_2 and x_3, we had made a poor guess, say, setting both x_1 and x_2 equal to zero. The capacity restrictions would then require:

$$1.5x_3 + 3.5x_4 = 275$$
$$3.0x_3 + 1.0x_4 = 300 \tag{3-4}$$

or
$$x_3 = \$ \ 86\tfrac{1}{9} \text{ thousand}$$
$$x_4 = \ \ 41\tfrac{2}{3} \text{ thousand}$$

and   Total payoff $= \overline{\$127\tfrac{7}{9}}$ thousand per month[1]

Since products C and D are the ones being produced, we know that z_3, the opportunity cost of producing a unit of item C, must just equal the \$1,000 payoff, p_3, from a unit of that item, and that similarly $z_4 = p_4 = \$1,000$. Or recalling (2-9) and (2-10),

$$z_3 = 1.5u_1 + 3.0u_2 = \$1,000$$
$$z_4 = 3.5u_1 + 1.0u_2 = \$1,000 \tag{3-5}$$

Solving for u_1 and u_2,

$$u_1 = \$222 \text{ per extrusion press hour}$$
$$u_2 = \$222 \text{ per annealing capacity hour}$$

These values of u_1 and u_2 differ radically from those obtained when items B and C were produced. The difference arises, of course, from the fact that in the one case we determined u_1 and u_2 by setting $z_3 = z_4 = \$1,000$ and that in the other we determined them from the condition that $z_2 = z_3 = \$1,000$. The implicit value of the two kinds of capacity closely depends upon which pair of products is being produced.

---

[1] As an exercise, construct on Fig. 2-3 the iso-payoff line associated with this algebraic solution.

Now we are ready to put the implicit prices u_1 and u_2 to work. The opportunity costs $z_1, \ldots, z_4$ are defined by

$$z_1 = 4.0u_1 + 0u_2 = \$888 \text{ per unit of item } A$$
$$z_2 = 2.0u_1 + 1.5u_2 = \$778 \text{ per unit of item } B$$
$$z_3 = 1.5u_1 + 3.0u_2 = \$1,000 \text{ per unit of item } C$$
$$z_4 = 3.5u_1 + 1.0u_2 = \$1,000 \text{ per unit of item } D$$

It should come as no surprise that z_3 and z_4 both equal \$1,000. These quantities were evaluated here simply as an arithmetic check upon our solution of equations (3-5). The values of z_1 and z_2, however, do constitute genuinely new pieces of information. They tell us that the opportunity cost, or incremental value, of the equipment absorbed in producing a unit of items A and B is, respectively, \$888 and \$778. Each of these lies below the unit payoffs, p_1 and p_2, of \$1,000, and so either product would increase the mill's total profits beyond the current level of \$127⅑ thousand per month.

Since $p_1 - z_1 = \$1,000 - 888 < p_2 - z_2 = \$1,000 - 778$, it seems like a good bet that product B will prove to be a more profitable change in the product mix than A. In other words, if faced with a choice of increasing the output of either A or B beyond zero, but not both, the implicit price calculation suggests that we choose B and delete either C or D from the mix. From our previous graphical analysis, we know which one has to be deleted, namely, item D. But if we are determined to proceed algebraically, as we must when large-scale problems are being studied, we shall have to deny ourselves the use of this knowledge. Instead we rewrite the capacity restriction equations (2-4) and (2-5) in the following form:

$$\begin{aligned} 2.0x_2' + 1.5x_3' + 3.5x_4' &= 275 \\ 1.5x_2' + 3.0x_3' + 1.0x_4' &= 300 \end{aligned} \tag{3-6}$$

where x_2' denotes the new value of the output of item B, x_3' the new value of item C, and x_4' the new value of D. (We know in advance that either x_3' or x_4' will turn out to be zero.) Here it will be convenient to construct three new variables, θ, Δ_3, and

Δ_4, as follows:

$$\theta = x_2' \qquad\qquad x_2' = \theta$$

$$\Delta_3 = \frac{x_3' - x_3}{\theta} \qquad \text{or} \qquad x_3' = x_3 + \Delta_3\theta \qquad (3\text{-}7)$$

$$\Delta_4 = \frac{x_4' - x_4}{\theta} \qquad\qquad x_4' = x_4 + \Delta_4\theta$$

According to these definitions, θ is just another name for the output of item B; and Δ_3 and Δ_4 are, respectively, the change in the output of items C and D per unit increase in the output of B. Equations (3-6) can be rewritten:

$$2.0\theta + 1.5(x_3 + \Delta_3\theta) + 3.5(x_4 + \Delta_4\theta) = 275$$
$$1.5\theta + 3.0(x_3 + \Delta_3\theta) + 1.0(x_4 + \Delta_4\theta) = 300 \qquad (3\text{-}8)$$

From (3-8), we subtract equations (3-4), which were used in order to determine x_3 and x_4 in the first place:

$$2.0\theta + 1.5\ \Delta_3\theta + 3.5\ \Delta_4\theta = 0$$
$$1.5\theta + 3.0\ \Delta_3\theta + 1.0\ \Delta_4\theta = 0$$

Dividing through by θ and transposing terms, we have two simultaneous conditions determining Δ_3 and Δ_4:

$$1.5\ \Delta_3 + 3.5\ \Delta_4 = -2.0$$
$$3.0\ \Delta_3 + 1.0\ \Delta_4 = -1.5$$

Solving these, we find

$$\Delta_3 = -13\!\!\not{3}6$$
$$\Delta_4 = -5\!\!\not{1}2$$

In other words, for each unit by which we increase the total output of product B, we shall have to cut down on items C and D by $13\!\!\not{3}6$ and $5\!\!\not{1}2$ of a unit, respectively. By cutting back in this way, we shall release just enough extrusion press time and annealing capacity to make possible the 1-unit increase in product B.

Definitions (3-7) can now be employed for calculating the new values of the unknowns, x_2', x_3', and x_4':

$$x_2' = \theta$$
$$x_3' = x_3 + \Delta_3\theta = 86\tfrac{1}{9} - 13\!\!\not{3}6\,\theta \qquad (3\text{-}9)$$
$$x_4' = x_4 + \Delta_4\theta = 41\tfrac{2}{3} - 5\!\!\not{1}2\,\theta$$

We still do not know how large θ ($= x_2'$ = the output of product B) can be made. From (3-9), however, we observe that the larger the value of θ, the lower become the values of both x_3' and x_4'. If we ask ourselves how large θ could grow before x_3' were driven down to zero, we would have

$$x_3' = x_3 + \Delta_3\theta = 0$$

or

$$\theta = \frac{x_3}{-\Delta_3} = \frac{86\frac{1}{9}}{13\frac{3}{36}} = 238\frac{6}{13}$$

Similarly, if x_4' is to be driven to zero,

$$\theta = \frac{x_4}{-\Delta_4} = \frac{41\frac{2}{3}}{5\frac{1}{12}} = 100$$

Because of the profitability of item B, the object now is to increase θ to the maximum extent, subject always to the proviso that x_3' and x_4' never become negative. Our calculations reveal that item D will vanish from the product mix when θ is only 100 but that the output of C will not disappear until θ reaches $238\frac{6}{13}$. Algebraically, then, a way has been found to determine what we already knew from geometrical reasoning: Product D has to be dropped from the product mix. Once we know that $\theta = 100$, equations (3-9) can be used in order to calculate the new values of our unknowns:

$$x_2' = \theta = 100$$
$$x_3' = x_3 + \Delta_3\theta = 86\frac{1}{9} - (13\frac{3}{36})(100) = 50$$
$$x_4' = x_4 + \Delta_4\theta = 41\frac{2}{3} - (5\frac{1}{12})(100) = 0$$

and   Total payoff = \$150 thousand per month

At long last, we have come around a full cycle. The simplex process has enabled us to arrive back at the original optimal product mix. The tentative solution involving products C and D yielded a payoff of just under \$128 thousand per month in comparison with the optimal level of \$150 thousand. In this instance, we were fortunate enough to have had a good starting position, and so we attained optimality in just one step. With more advanced problems, even though the principles of solution are identical, the same good luck cannot be expected. Quite a few steps or iterations may be needed before an optimal solution is produced.

More definitions

In the system of input-output relationships (3-2), we previously observed that there were n unknowns and m equations, with $n > m$. If, when we set $n - m$ of the unknowns equal to zero, it is possible to solve the m equations *uniquely* for nonnegative values of the m remaining unknowns, the resulting m values are said to form a "basic feasible solution."

Example. When x_3 is set equal to zero, it is possible to solve the following equations uniquely for x_1 and x_2:

$$x_1 + 2x_2 + 6x_3 = 50$$
$$2x_1 + 3x_2 + 9x_3 = 80$$
$$x_1 = 10 \qquad x_2 = 20 \qquad x_3 = 0$$

If, however, x_1 is set equal to zero, this system becomes

$$2x_2 + 6x_3 = 50$$
$$3x_2 + 9x_3 = 80$$

There are no values of x_2 and x_3 that will simultaneously satisfy this last pair of equations. Hence, although x_1 and x_2 constitute a basic feasible set of unknowns, x_2 and x_3 do not make up such a set. Again, in the following system x_2 and x_3 do not form a basic feasible set—here because there are an infinite number of values which satisfy:

$$2x_2 + 6x_3 = 50$$
$$3x_2 + 9x_3 = 75$$

Why do we take such an interest in basic feasible solutions? There is just one reason for this interest: One or more basic feasible solutions will necessarily be optimal. This fact greatly narrows down the class of possible alternative solutions to be examined. The simplex method is nothing but a systematic procedure for moving from one basic feasible solution to another, each step being made in the direction of an increase in payoff.

A remark must be inserted parenthetically here. The optimal solution to a linear programming problem is not necessarily unique. There may be many optimal solutions, each with the same level of payoff. In the brass mill problem, for example, there might well have been a fifth product with inputs of $1\frac{1}{6}$ hours of extrusion press time and 2 hours of annealing capacity per $1 thousand worth of output. A payoff of $150 thousand per month could then have been produced by concentrating upon this product alone or by turning this one out along with products B and C. A one-product, two-product, or three-product mix would be equally optimal. This example does not contradict the theorem just stated. There *is* a two-product mix—a basic feasible solution—among the class of all optimal solutions.

Just a few more definitions are needed before the simplex procedure can be characterized in general terms. The column of input and output coefficients associated with an unknown x_j is said to be the jth "vector," or "activity." The rectangular array formed by placing all n columns next to one another is termed a "matrix." And the square array formed by the m individual columns of a basic feasible solution is a special matrix known as a "basis." The matrix of the brass mill problem is, of course,

$$
\begin{array}{cccc}
4.0 & 2.0 & 1.5 & 3.5 \\
0 & 1.5 & 3.0 & 1.0
\end{array}
$$

The second activity, for example, in this matrix consists of the *column* of input coefficients associated with the output of $1 thousand worth of product B:

2.0 hours of extrusion press time
1.5 hours of annealing capacity

Since the optimal solution was obtained by setting $x_1 = x_4 = 0$ and solving for x_2 and x_3, it is the second and third columns of the original matrix that are collectively said to represent an optimal basis:

$$
\begin{array}{cc}
2.0 & 1.5 \\
1.5 & 3.0
\end{array}
$$

The "basis theorem" of linear programming is the name given to the proposition that, among the class of all optimal solutions, there will be at least one that constitutes a basic feasible solution.

A summary

With these definitions, the individual steps of the simplex procedure can be summarized as follows (see flow diagram 3-1):

1. Of the total of n unknowns, set $n - m$ of them equal to zero and solve (3-2) for values of the remaining m.   It will be assumed

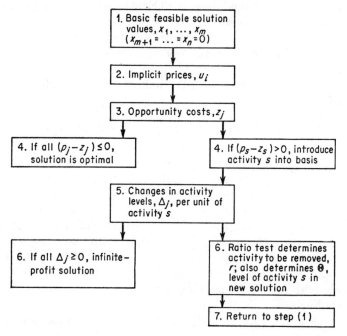

Fig. 3-1. Flow diagram for simplex computations.

that the resulting values of the x_j are unique and that none are negative, i.e., that some basic feasible solution to the linear programming problem can be obtained by direct inspection.   For convenience in notation, it will be useful to number the activities in such a way that the basis consists of activities 1, 2, ..., m and that the unknowns $x_{m+1}, x_{m+2}, \ldots, x_n$ are the ones that have been equated to zero.

2. Solve for the implicit prices $u_1, u_2, \ldots, u_i, \ldots, u_m$ by noting the requirement that, if activity j is in the basis, then z_j, the opportunity cost of using that activity, must equal p_j, the unit payoff from the activity:

$$\sum_{i=1}^{m} a_{ij} u_i = p_j \qquad j = 1, 2, \ldots, m \qquad (3\text{-}10)$$

Since both the a_{ij} and the p_j coefficients are known numbers, the system (3-10) may be solved directly for the unknowns u_i. Moreover, since activities 1, ..., m are said to constitute a basis, the resulting values of the u_i are necessarily unique.

3. Employ the implicit prices just calculated in order to determine z_j, the opportunity cost per unit of the jth activity outside the basis:

$$z_j = \sum_{i=1}^{m} a_{ij} u_i \qquad j = m + 1, m + 2, \ldots, n$$

4. Compute the difference $p_j - z_j$ between the unit payoff and the opportunity cost for each of these activities. If there are no activities for which this difference is positive, the simplex process can be terminated. An optimal solution has been determined. Otherwise, determine which of these positive differences is greatest, and label the corresponding activity with the subscript s. The implicit pricing criterion says that it is profitable for this activity to be substituted in place of one of those in the existing basis and for the remaining activity levels to be adjusted accordingly.

5. Denoting by x_j' the values of the unknowns in the new basic solution,

$$\sum_{j=1}^{m} a_{ij} x_j = q_i = \sum_{j=1}^{m} a_{ij} x_j' + a_{is} x_s'$$

$$= \sum_{j=1}^{m} a_{ij}(x_j + \Delta_j \theta) + a_{is} \theta \qquad i = 1, \ldots, m$$

or
$$\sum_{j=1}^{m} a_{ij} \Delta_j = -a_{is} \qquad i = 1, \ldots, m \qquad (3\text{-}11)$$

This set (3-11) may now be solved for values of Δ_j, the change in each of the basis variables per unit increase in the level of activity s.

6. By definition:

$$x'_j = x_j + \Delta_j \theta \qquad j = 1, \ldots, m \qquad (3\text{-}12)$$

Consequently, if $\Delta_j \geq 0$, then no matter how large θ becomes, x'_j cannot drop below zero. The activity to be removed from the basis and labeled with the subscript r must therefore be one for which $\Delta_j < 0$.* Among these, it can be found by searching for the one for which the ratio $x_j / -\Delta_j$ is smallest. The smallest of these ratios indicates the maximum value that can be assigned to θ without driving any of the altered activity levels below zero. At the same time, this ratio test determines which of the activities is to be labeled r and removed from the basis.

7. Knowing both Δ_j and θ, we now employ (3-12) to calculate the new values x'_j. By definition, $x'_s = \theta$. The payoff of our new basic feasible solution differs from that of the old one by

$$\theta \left(p_s + \sum_{j=1}^{m} p_j \Delta_j \right) = \theta(p_s - z_s).\dagger \quad \text{Since} \quad \theta \quad \text{can} \quad \text{ordinarily} \quad \text{be}$$

* If all $\Delta_j \geq 0$, the payoff can be increased without limit. In any well-behaved problem, at least one of the Δ_j will be negative.

† During the one iteration of the brass mill problem described earlier, we found $p_s - z_s = p_2 - z_2 = \$1,000 - 778 = \$222$ per unit of product B. Since the value of θ was 100, we had $\theta(p_s - z_s) = \$22.2$ thousand. This figure, of course, checks with the difference in payoff before and after the iteration—respectively, \$127.8 thousand and \$150 thousand.

The reader who possesses some familiarity with matrix notation may find it instructive to go through the following proofs. First, we shall prove that, in general,

$$\sum_{j=1}^{m} p_j \Delta_j = -z_s = -\sum_{i=1}^{m} a_{is} u_i$$

Let B denote the basis matrix, u the row vector of implicit prices u_i, and p the row vector of profitability coefficients p_j for the activities within the given a positive value,[1] the new solution, although not necessarily optimal, will have a higher payoff than the previous one.

With this improved solution, we now return to step 1 of the simplex process and continue in an iterative fashion until we reach a basis that satisfies the optimality criterion of step 4 or the infinite-profit criterion of step 6.   The simplex procedure neces-

---

basis.   Also, let A_s represent the column vector of input-output coefficients a_{is} for activity s, and let Δ represent the column vector of the adjustments Δ_j per unit of activity s.

By definition of u, $\quad\quad uB = p$
By definition of Δ, $\quad\quad B\Delta = -A_s$
Therefore, $\quad\quad p\Delta = (uB)\Delta = u(B\Delta) = -uA_s$

or
$$\sum_{j=1}^{m} p_j \Delta_j = -\sum_{i=1}^{m} a_{is}u_i$$

Second, we shall establish that $\sum_{j=1}^{m} p_j x_j = \sum_{i=1}^{m} u_i q_i$.   In an economist's language, this means that the returns imputed to each factor of production will exactly equal the total returns to the enterprise.   For example, in the brass mill optimal solution,

$$\sum_{j=1}^{m} p_j x_j = \$1,000x_2 + \$1,000x_3 = \$150 \text{ thousand}$$

and
$$\sum_{i=1}^{m} u_i q_i = u_1(275) + u_2(300) = \$150 \text{ thousand}$$

In order to prove this "exhaustion-of-product" theorem, let x and q represent, respectively, the column vectors of activity levels x_j and of availabilities q_i.

Again, by definition of u, $\quad\quad uB = p$
If the basis satisfies (3-2), $\quad\quad Bx = q$
Therefore, $\quad\quad px = (uB)x = u(Bx) = uq$

or
$$\sum_{j=1}^{m} p_j x_j = \sum_{i=1}^{m} u_i q_i$$

---

[1] If θ equals zero, we have come across a case known technically as "degeneracy."   More will be said about this in the Appendix to the next chapter.

sarily ends in a finite number of iterations, ordinarily in no more steps than twice m, the number of equations. Through the aid of electronic computers, it is perfectly feasible to solve problems involving hundreds of equations and thousands of activities.

A petroleum refining example

To illustrate the application of the simplex procedure without relying upon any illegitimate foreknowledge about the optimal solution, we shall conclude with an example drawn from the area of petroleum refining—again an example that is drastically simplified in order to illustrate the fundamentals involved.

In this case, the refiner is faced with just one type of physical capacity limitation—the crude oil input capacity of his plant, 50 thousand barrels of oil per day (abbreviated 50 MB/D). In addition to this physical limitation, he also faces a marketing restriction. He must provide 27 MB/D of motor gasoline for sale in the company's service stations. No specific marketing limitations affect the sale of any of the other refinery products.

The options confronting the refiner are of three kinds: (1) to operate the plant for a low yield of gasoline and a high yield of other products, (2) to operate for a high yield of gasoline, and (3) to supplement the refinery's own gasoline output with material purchased on the open market. The physical yields and economic evaluations of these three alternatives are summarized in Table 3-1.[1] After just a brief inspection of the unit payoffs shown on this table, the casual observer is sorely tempted to say that the third alternative—outside purchase—looks so unprofitable that it can be omitted from further consideration. The payoff per barrel from this activity is so much lower than on the first two that it does not appear to be a likely choice at all. On the

[1] As far as this one problem is concerned, the refiner need not have bothered ascertaining the selling value of motor gasoline. His output plus purchases of the product is fixed at 27 MB/D. His gross income from the one source will therefore be independent of any decisions open to him. This analysis really consists of finding out how to supply the gasoline requirement at minimum cost, taking account of by-product credits.

off-chance that outside purchase might be a profitable thing, however, we shall retain it in our linear programming analysis.

TABLE 3-1. THREE ALTERNATIVE OIL REFINING POSSIBILITIES

	1. Low gasoline yield operation	2. High gasoline yield operation	3. Outside purchase
Yields per barrel of crude oil:			
Motor gasoline	.40 barrel	.60 barrel	
Other products	.60 barrel	.30 barrel	
Unit contribution to profit and overhead*	$1.20 per barrel of crude oil = .40($6.00) + .60($4.00) − $3.00 − $.60	$1.00 per barrel of crude oil = .60($6.00) + .30($4.00) − $3.00 − $.80	$.80 per barrel of gasoline purchased = $6.00 − $5.20

* Refinery selling values: $6 per barrel of motor gasoline sold; $4 per barrel of other products sold.

Refinery costs: $3 per barrel of crude oil purchased; $5.20 per barrel of motor gasoline purchased; $.60 per barrel of crude oil (processing costs on low gasoline yield operation); $.80 per barrel of crude oil (processing costs on high gasoline yield operation).

This is a model in which we shall let x_1 denote the number of thousands of barrels of crude oil processed for a low gasoline yield, x_2 the number processed for a high yield, and x_3 the number of thousands of barrels of gasoline purchased from outside sources. The payoff equation and other conditions may be expressed as follows:

Maximize the payoff =

$$\$1.20x_1 + \$1.00x_2 + \$.80x_3 \tag{3-13}$$

subject to the conditions:

$$x_1 + x_2 \leq 50 \tag{3-14}$$
$$.40x_1 + .60x_2 + x_3 = 27 \tag{3-15}$$
and $$x_1, x_2, x_3 \geq 0 \tag{3-16}$$

Before going on with the simplex procedure, we shall find it useful to introduce two new unknowns into the problem, respectively termed a "slack" and an "artificial" variable.   A slack variable, x_4, will have to be introduced into (3-14), the crude oil intake limitation, in order to convert it from an *in*equality into an equality.   Why not simply require that $x_1 + x_2 = 50$?   Because if the payoff on the second activity were sufficiently great, it would pay to meet the entire marketing requirement by processing just 45 MB/D of crude oil for a maximum gasoline yield and by leaving 5 MB/D of crude oil capacity unused.   For this reason, we define the nonnegative unknown x_4 as the amount of unused crude oil processing capacity, and in general we shall refer to it as a slack variable or as a disposal activity.   Condition (3-14) now becomes:

$$x_1 + x_2 + x_4 = 50 \qquad (3\text{-}14a)$$

A slack activity, then, is introduced for good economic reasons —to take account of the possibility that a suspected bottleneck point may not turn out to be a bottleneck after all.   An "artificial" activity, by contrast, is introduced for purely computational reasons—to make sure that we have a basic feasible solution to begin with.   In any equation for which we do not already have a slack variable such as x_4, we may insert an artificial one solely for the purpose of finding an initial solution.   Here we need introduce only one artificial variable, x_5, into the problem.   Equation (3-15) is rewritten:

$$.40x_1 + .60x_2 + x_3 + x_5 = 27 \qquad (3\text{-}15a)$$

By now, the reader will have noticed that, if we let our initial basis consist exclusively of slack and artificial activities, the starting solution may be written by inspection: $x_1 = x_2 = x_3 = 0$; $x_4 = 50$; and $x_5 = 27$.   This is a basic feasible solution that satisfies all requirements of step 1 of the simplex process.

As welcome as an artificial vector is in an initial basis, it is an unmitigated nuisance as far as any physical interpretation is concerned.   Our starting solution is truly of a do-nothing variety. It says that we should dispose not only of the 50 MB/D of refining capacity but also of the 27 MB/D of gasoline requirements.   The first of these possibilities is an economically legitimate one, but the second is not.   Even if we wish to, we cannot avoid meeting the sales commitment. We must ensure, therefore, that the artificial variable x_5 does not appear at a positive level in the final optimal solution. To do this, it will be enough to place a large penalty upon its use—a negative payoff of, say, \$10 per barrel of unsatisfied marketing requirements for gasoline. The new payoff expression becomes

$$\$1.20x_1 + \$1.00x_2 + \$.80x_3 - \$10.00x_5 \qquad (3\text{-}13a)$$

Table 3-2 summarizes the data of (3-13a) to (3-15a)—the payoff coefficients p_j, the input-output coefficients a_{ij}, and the right-hand-side constants q_i of the refinery problem. An initial solution is also noted on this table—the basis variables x_4 and x_5 at levels of 50 and 27, respectively. Activities 1 to 3 are all, at this stage, outside the basis. It is now possible to begin step 2 of the simplex procedure outlined earlier.

TABLE 3-2. OIL REFINERY MATRIX AND INITIAL SOLUTION

	Activity j					Right-hand-side constants q_i
	1	2	3	4	5	
Payoff coefficients p_j (3-13a)	1.20	1.00	.80	0	−10.00	
Equation (3-14a), a_{1j}	1.00	1.00	0	1.00	0	50
Equation (3-15a), a_{2j}	.40	.60	1.00	0	1.00	27
x_j	*	*	*	50	27	

* Activity not in basis.

To determine the implicit prices u_1 and u_2 associated with the processing capacity and the marketing limitations, we equate the opportunity cost of the activities in the basis to the unit payoffs:

$$z_4 = 1.00u_1 + 0u_2 = 0$$
$$z_5 = 0u_1 + 1.00u_2 = -10.00$$

Therefore $\qquad u_1 = 0 \qquad u_2 = -10.00$

Knowing the implicit prices, u_1 and u_2, we may evaluate z_1, z_2, and z_3, the opportunity cost of those activities outside the current basis. The implicit prices u_i and the differences $p_j - z_j$ are shown in Table 3-3. Since these differences are positive in each of the first three columns, the introduction of any one of the activities 1, 2, or 3 into the basis will be profitable. Furthermore, since activity 3 (outside purchase of motor gasoline) indicates the greatest potential unit gain, this is the one designated as activity s—the one to be substituted in place of one of those currently in the basis.

**TABLE 3-3. OIL REFINERY PROBLEM; STEPS 2 TO 4
OF FIRST ITERATION**

	Activity j					Right-hand-side constants q_i	Implicit prices u_i
	1	2	3	4	5		
p_j	1.20	1.00	.80	0	−10.00		
$(p_j - z_j)$	5.20	7.00	10.80	0	0		
a_{1j}	1.00	1.00	0	1.00	0	50	0
a_{2j}	.40	.60	1.00	0	1.00	27	−10.00
x_j	*	*	*	50	27		

* Activity not in basis.

According to step 5 of the simplex summary, next comes the determination of the Δ_j, the changes in activity levels per unit increase in θ, the new level of activity 3. This is accomplished by solving the system:

$$1.00\,\Delta_4 + 0\,\Delta_5 = -0$$
$$0\,\Delta_4 + 1.00\,\Delta_5 = -1.00$$
Therefore $\quad \Delta_4 = 0 \quad\quad \Delta_5 = -1.00$

Step 6 tells us how to calculate θ, the number of barrels of outside gasoline purchased (see Table 3-4). Among those Δ_j that are negative, compute the ratio $x_j/-\Delta_j$. (This ratio cannot be negative.)   The smallest of these ratios equals θ, the maximum permissible level of activity s.   In our numerical example, only one of the Δ_j values is negative, Δ_5.   Calculating the ratio $x_5/-\Delta_5$, it can be seen that θ, the number of thousands of barrels purchased, must equal 27.   From this value, along with the Δ_j, we may readily solve for the activity levels in our new basis by applying the definition $x'_j = x_j + \Delta_j\theta$.   Note that this automatically implies a zero value for x'_5, the level of activity r, the one being removed in order to form the new basis.

TABLE 3-4. OIL REFINERY PROBLEM; STEPS 5 TO 7
OF FIRST ITERATION

	Activity j					Right-hand-side constants q_i
	1	2	3	4	5	
a_{1j}	1.00	1.00	0	1.00	0	50
a_{2j}	.40	.60	1.00	0	1.00	27
x_j	*	*	*	50	27	$\sum\limits_{j=1}^{5} p_j x_j = -\$270.0$ thousand per day
θ, Δ_j			θ	0	−1.00	
$x_j/-\Delta_j$ (negative Δ_j only)				.....	$27 = \theta$	
$x'_j = x_j + \Delta_j\theta$	*	*	27	50	*	$\sum\limits_{j=1}^{5} p_j x'_j = \$21.6$ thousand per day

* Activity not in basis.

Multiplying prices and activity levels together, we may compare the total refinery payoff before and after the change in basis. The total has increased from the negative amount of $270.0 thousand per day to the positive one of $21.6 thousand. This is all just as predicted by the expression $\theta(p_3 - z_3) = 27(\$10.80) = \$291.6$ thousand per day.

With the new activity levels, we are ready to begin the second iteration.   As before, the first order of business is to solve for the implicit prices u_i and then to employ these for the purpose of computing the opportunity costs z_j (see Table 3-5). In this iteration, only two of the computed differences $p_j - z_j$ are positive—those associated with activities 1 and 2. Since $p_1 - z_1$ is the larger of the two, activity 1 (the low gasoline yield operation) is labeled s, the one to be substituted in place of one of those in the current basis. The unit changes in activity levels Δ_3 and Δ_4 are again determined by solving a system of simultaneous equations:

$$0\,\Delta_3 + 1.00\,\Delta_4 = -1.00$$
$$1.00\,\Delta_3 + 0\,\Delta_4 = -.40$$

Therefore $\qquad \Delta_3 = -.40 \qquad \Delta_4 = -1.00$

TABLE 3-5. OIL REFINERY PROBLEM; SECOND ITERATION

	Activity j					Right-hand-side constants q_i	Implicit prices u_i
	1	2	3	4	5		
p_j	1.20	1.00	.80	0	−10.00		
$(p_j - z_j)$	.88	.52	0	0	−10.80		
a_{1j}	1.00	1.00	0	1.00	0	50	0
a_{2j}	.40	.60	1.00	0	1.00	27	.80
x_j	*	*	27	50	*	$\sum_{j=1}^{5} p_j x_j = \$21.6$ thousand per day	
$\theta,\ \Delta_j$	θ		−.40	−1.00			
$x_j/-\Delta_j$ (negative Δ_j only)			67.5	50.0 = θ			
$x_j' = x_j + \Delta_j\theta$	50	*	7	*	*	$\sum_{j=1}^{5} p_j x_j' = \$65.6$ thousand per day	

* Activity not in basis.

To find the value of θ, the number of barrels of crude oil processed by method 1, we compute the ratios $x_j/-\Delta_j$. On this iteration, both Δ_3 and Δ_4 are negative, i.e., both activities 3 and 4 must be curtailed with an increase in the level of activity 1. Comparing the ratios, $x_3/-\Delta_3$ and $x_4/-\Delta_4$, it is found that the latter is the smaller of the two. If θ were forced above the level of 50, this would necessitate disposing of a negative number of barrels of crude oil processing capacity. We therefore set θ equal to 50, drop the disposal vector from the basis, and compute the new activity levels, x'_j. This completes the second iteration—one which was accompanied by an increase in payoff from \$21.6 thousand to \$65.6 thousand per day.

Table 3-6 contains the implicit prices and the $p_j - z_j$ differences for the new basis. Since none of these differences are positive, the current solution is an optimal one and the simplex process may be terminated.

TABLE 3-6. OIL REFINERY PROBLEM; THIRD ITERATION AND OPTIMAL SOLUTION

	Activity j					Right-hand-side constants q_i	Implicit prices u_i
	1	2	3	4	5		
p_j	1.20	1.00	.80	0	−10.00		
$(p_j - z_j)$	0	−.36	0	−.88	−10.80		
a_{1j}	1.00	1.00	0	1.00	0	50	.88
a_{2j}	.40	.60	1.00	0	1.00	27	.80
x_j	50	*	7	*	*	$\sum\limits_{j=1}^{5} p_j x_j = \$65.6$ thousand per day	

* Activity not in basis.

The optimal activity levels x_j have an obvious enough physical interpretation. Both the slack and the artificial vectors are excluded from the optimal program. The refinery's entire crude oil capacity is employed on the low-yield gasoline process, and just enough additional gasoline is purchased on the outside market to supply the sales requirement. So much for obvious ways of ruling out economic alternatives! Had outside purchases been eliminated from consideration, the total attainable payoff would have been sharply reduced (see exercise 3-1).

Even more interesting than the optimal physical program (the x_j values) are the implicit prices, the u_i appearing in Table 3-6. Equation (3-14a), it will be recalled, constitutes a restriction upon crude oil intake capacity. The fact that u_1 is \$.88 per barrel of daily capacity means that we have here a measure of the worth of additional equipment. Each additional barrel of capacity would be worth \$.88 per day. The additional equipment would all be used to reduce the reliance upon open-market purchases of gasoline. For every barrel of additional crude capacity, these purchases could be cut by .40 barrels of gasoline, a net saving of \$.88 per barrel of crude capacity.

The value of u_2 has a similar interpretation—one connected with a marketing restriction rather than with a physical capacity limit. Equation (3-15a) specifies that only 27 MB/D of gasoline are to be sold in the company's retail outlets. The fact that u_2 is \$.80 per barrel of daily gasoline sales means that, for every barrel by which the company could enlarge its gasoline market, the overall profits would increase by \$.80 per day. Knowing this magnitude, we are in a far better position than otherwise to judge the value of marketing efforts. Should the selling campaign required to produce an additional barrel of sales cost less than \$.80, the implicit price indicates that this will be a worthwhile move; otherwise it will not be.

The implicit prices that we have been calculating resemble break-even points. They are yardsticks by which we may measure what it will be worth to us if we succeed in altering the restrictions initially stipulated for our economic model. The more arbitrary these stipulations, the more important it is for us to be able to explore the implications of changing them. If linear programming provided nothing but a more reliable framework for estimating incremental costs and values, this alone would justify its importance to management.

EXERCISES

3-1. Suppose that outside purchases of gasoline were excluded from consideration in the oil refinery problem just discussed.

Set up the appropriate linear programming matrix, and solve by
the simplex method. By how much do you find the over-all
company profits reduced?

3-2. Return to the optimal solution of the refinery problem
shown in Table 3-6. By how much would the unit payoff on
activity 2 (the high-yield gasoline operation) have to rise in order
for it to be profitable for the company to use this method of
operation at all? By how much would this coefficient have to rise
in order for the entire gasoline requirement to be satisfied by using
this one activity? Be sure to justify your answers.

3-3. Refer back to the capital budgeting problem discussed at
the beginning of Chapter 2. Formulate this algebraically as a
linear programming problem, and solve by the simplex method.

3-4. Refer back to the fertilizer-manufacturing example of the
preceding chapter (exercise 2-4). Suppose that the manufacturer wants to put out a product that weighs just 100 pounds per
bag and that still satisfies the nitrogen and phosphate content
specifications. Set this up as a linear programming problem, and
solve using the simplex method.

3-5. A farm family owns 60 acres of land and has $6,000 in
funds available for investment. Its members can produce a total
of 2,500 man-hours worth of labor during the winter months and
3,500 man-hours during the summer.[1]

Cash income may be obtained from three crops and two types of
livestock: cows and laying hens. No investment funds are
needed for the crops. However, a herd of 8 cows will require an
investment outlay of $8,000, and a flock of 1,000 hens will
require $4,000.

An 8-cow herd will require 20 acres of land, 500 man-hours of
work during the winter months, and another 500 man-hours during the summer. The cows will produce a net annual cash income
of $2,000 for the family. The corresponding figures for a flock of

---

[1] This problem is adapted from a considerably more realistic and complex
study by C. E. Bishop, "Programming Farm-Nonfarm Allocation of Farm
Family Resources," *Journal of Farm Economics*, May, 1956.

1,000 layers are: no acreage, 600 man-hours during the winter, 600 more man-hours during the summer, and an annual net cash income of $1,600.

Estimated man-hours and income per acre planted in each of the three crops are as follows:

	Cotton	Corn	Oats
Winter man-hours.............	0	5	0
Summer man-hours............	100	15	10
Net annual cash income........	$230	$60	$40

If the family wishes to maximize its net cash income, how much acreage should it plant in each of the crops, and how many cows and hens should be kept? What is the economic significance to the family of the implicit prices you have computed?

Hints. 1. For your model, you may assume the existence of fractional herds and flocks.

2. Try to start your simplex calculation with a good guess, rather than with a do-nothing basis.

CHAPTER FOUR

THE TRANSPORTATION MODEL

A steel distribution problem

In this chapter, our attention will be confined to a rather specialized application of linear programming—one known as the "transportation" model. This is a case in which the simplex calculation turns out to have certain remarkable properties both from the viewpoint of paper-and-pencil computations and from that of economic analysis. Much of the interest in this model lies in the fact that an almost identical approach seems suitable for certain problems in production scheduling over time—problems which on the surface bear no resemblance to the physical transportation of goods.

The initial case to be studied will be that of the Ajax Steel Company, an integrated steel producer faced with distribution choices similar to those described by the first chart in this volume (Figure 1-1). In the two-mill, two-warehouse case indicated by that figure, little more than mental arithmetic is needed in order to figure out the best way to assign mills to customers. With several mills and several warehouses in the picture, with limited output capabilities, and with costs dependent upon water as well as upon land mileage, simple intuition no longer seems very satisfactory. Things become still further complicated if any account is to be taken of the cost differences existing between individual plants.

In our linear programming model, we shall assume that Ajax owns three mills (Allentown, Birmingham, and Chicago) and that it supplies finished products to four warehouses (1, 2, 3, and 4). The weekly production capacities available at the three mills are, respectively, 50 thousand, 20 thousand, and 20 thousand tons—a total of 90 thousand for the company as a whole. This over-all capability is more than adequate to meet the total requirements of 76 thousand. Total requirements are broken down as follows:

Warehouse 1	12
Warehouse 2	21
Warehouse 3	32
Warehouse 4	11
Total	76 thousand tons per week

Two interrelated questions then arise: (1) What should be the total output at each mill? (2) Which mills ought to supply the four individual warehouses? Both questions pose an economic choice, and in order to analyze the alternatives, we need some knowledge of the cost factors involved.

A digression on cost estimating

As in most economic analysis, the cost factors employed here are understood to be incremental ones. Necessarily they exclude any allowance for costs that will be *un*affected by the choices that we might want to recommend. It is for this reason that depreciation and mill overhead charges do not enter into the reckoning of our cost coefficients. By the same logic, basic research and development laboratory activities ought not be charged against the incremental costs of a producing mill, although its own quality control laboratory would be a legitimate item.

When we say then that the production of an additional ton at the Allentown mill will cost $58, what we mean is that $58 could

be saved by Ajax as a whole if output at that mill were to be cut
back by 1 ton.   This is, of course, a distinctly different concept of
costs from the one traditionally employed in financial accounting.
The financial accountant's job is to present a historical record of
what has actually transpired.   The economic analyst is content
to let bygones be bygones and is concerned solely with estimating
the effect of current decisions upon avoidable future costs.   The
economist's work requires him to refrain studiously from spread-
ing past costs or fixed overhead commitments into future operations.   "Don't allocate the unallocable" is his motto.

Fixed costs, e.g., the cost of acquiring new equipment, become a
very relevant thing, of course, when long-term decisions are under
consideration.   At the time when the Ajax Steel Company is
about to construct a new rolling mill, the cost of acquiring that
mill is certainly not a fixed charge.   It is an expense that can be
avoided by the very simple expedient of not building the mill.
(For a typical capital-investment problem, see Chapter 6.)
Once the company is committed to the new plant and the problem
is simply one of utilizing equipment that is available in any case,
it is entirely proper to ignore depreciation accounting charges for
this equipment.   This is not to say that the implicit worth of all
capital equipment is zero, but rather that an implicit value cannot
be assigned easily to such equipment in isolation from the operating plan itself.

A steel distribution problem (initial solution)

Assuming that the incremental production costs have been
estimated at, say, $58 per ton for Allentown, we are still left with
the problem of comparing alternative routings.   Transport and
handling costs from Allentown to warehouse 1 might work out to
be $15 a ton.   We would then say that c_{A1}, the combined total of
production plus shipping costs, equals $73 per incremental ton.
The three-mill, four-customer array of combined costs is given
by Table 4-1.

Notice that the cost coefficient c_{A1} has two subscripts—the
first representing the mill of origin and the second the warehouse

destination.   Similarly, the unknowns x_j of our linear programming model will each have two subscripts.   The quantity x_{A1}, for example, will represent the number of thousands of tons of finished steel shipped weekly from Allentown to warehouse 1.   Now that

TABLE 4-1. INCREMENTAL SHIPPING AND
TRANSPORTATION COSTS

	Mill		
	Allentown	Birmingham	Chicago
Warehouse 1	$c_{A1} = \$73$	$c_{B1} = \$95$	$c_{C1} = \$71$
Warehouse 2	$c_{A2} = \$90$	$c_{B2} = \$89$	$c_{C2} = \$82$
Warehouse 3	$c_{A3} = \$97$	$c_{B3} = \$93$	$c_{C3} = \$100$
Warehouse 4	$c_{A4} = \$76$	$c_{B4} = \$94$	$c_{C4} = \$91$

the mill availabilities, the shipping requirements, and the cost factors have been specified, the rest is easy.   The Ajax linear programming model may be written:

$$\text{Minimize the cost} = 73x_{A1} + 90x_{A2} + 97x_{A3} + 76x_{A4}$$
$$+ 95x_{B1} + 89x_{B2} + 93x_{B3} + 94x_{B4}$$
$$+ 71x_{C1} + 82x_{C2} + 100x_{C3} + 91x_{C4} \quad (4\text{-}1)$$

subject to the conditions:

$$x_{A1} + x_{B1} + x_{C1} = 12 \quad (4\text{-}2)$$
$$x_{A2} + x_{B2} + x_{C2} = 21 \quad (4\text{-}3)$$
$$x_{A3} + x_{B3} + x_{C3} = 32 \quad (4\text{-}4)$$
$$x_{A4} + x_{B4} + x_{C4} = 11 \quad (4\text{-}5)$$
$$x_{A1} + x_{A2} + x_{A3} + x_{A4} \leq 50 \quad (4\text{-}6)$$
$$x_{B1} + x_{B2} + x_{B3} + x_{B4} \leq 20 \quad (4\text{-}7)$$
$$x_{C1} + x_{C2} + x_{C3} + x_{C4} \leq 20 \quad (4\text{-}8)$$
$$\text{and} \qquad x_j \geq 0 \quad (4\text{-}9)$$

In order to carry out the simplex routine, these data may be organized within an array, or "tableau," like Table 4-2A.   Our

TABLE 4-2A. AJAX STEEL SHIPPING PROBLEM

	Mill			Total requirements, thousands of tons
	Allentown	Birmingham	Chicago	
Warehouse 1	73⌐ x_{A1}	95⌐ x_{B1}	71⌐ x_{C1}	12
Warehouse 2	90⌐ x_{A2}	89⌐ x_{B2}	82⌐ x_{C2}	21
Warehouse 3	97⌐ x_{A3}	93⌐ x_{B3}	100⌐ x_{C3}	32
Warehouse 4	76⌐ x_{A4}	94⌐ x_{B4}	91⌐ x_{C4}	11
Warehouse 5 (excess capacity)	0⌐ x_{A5}	0⌐ x_{B5}	0⌐ x_{C5}	
Total capacity, thousands of tons	50	20	20	

TABLE 4-2B. AJAX STEEL SHIPPING PROBLEM; INITIAL ALLOCATIONS

	Mill			Total requirements, thousands of tons
	Allentown	Birmingham	Chicago	
Warehouse 1	73⌐	95⌐	71⌐ 12	12
Warehouse 2	90⌐	89⌐ 13	82⌐ 8	21
Warehouse 3	97⌐ 25	93⌐ 7	100⌐	32
Warehouse 4	76⌐ 11	94⌐	91⌐	11
Warehouse 5 (excess capacity)	0⌐ 14	0⌐	0⌐	
Total capacity, thousands of tons	50	20	20	

$$\sum_j c_j x_j = 97(25) + 76(11) + 0(14) + 89(13) + 93(7) + 71(12) + 82(8)$$
$$= \$6,577 \text{ thousand per week}$$

problem is to write entries in the individual boxes marked x_{A1}, x_{B1}, . . . in such a way that (1) the quantities entered in each row will sum up to the requirements at each of the four warehouses as specified by (4-2) to (4-5), and (2) the quantities entered in each column will sum up to the capacities at each of the three mills.

Note that, in transforming inequalities (4-6) to (4-8) into column-sum requirements, a fifth warehouse has been introduced —a fictitious one to account for the three slack variables x_{A5}, x_{B5}, and x_{C5}.* These three unknowns will denote, respectively, the unused capacity at Allentown, Birmingham, and Chicago.

To facilitate hand calculations, the cost coefficients c_{A1}, c_{B1}, etc., are maintained continuously on display in the upper left-hand corner of each box within the transportation array. In order to indicate that no incremental costs are associated with excess capacity, a cost coefficient of zero is entered within the three boxes reserved for the slack variables x_{A5}, x_{B5}, and x_{C5}.

Just as in all other simplex calculations, the basis theorem, together with the implicit prices concept, underlies our work. Here the basis theorem says that at each step the number of basis variables will equal seven—one for each of the four row-sum restrictions and one for each of the three columns of Table 4-2A. Furthermore, corresponding to each basic feasible solution, there will be seven implicit prices—one to measure the incremental worth of additional capacity of each of Ajax's three mills and one to measure the incremental cost of meeting delivery requirements at each of the four warehouses. At each iteration of the simplex process, these implicit prices are employed to check what can be done, if anything, to reduce the over-all costs specified by the cost equation (4-1).

In selecting a first feasible solution, any arbitrary procedure is permissible. One of the most satisfactory rules of thumb is to

---

* No row-sum restriction applies to these three unknowns. However, given our knowledge that the total capacity equals 90 thousand tons and that the requirements are only 76 thousand tons, we know that the sum of the three slack variables—the weekly total of unused capacity—will inevitably be 14 thousand tons.

scan Table 4-2A for the smallest cost coefficient, the next smallest coefficient, and so on, and then to allocate steel mill capacity in this same priority sequence. A priority procedure of this sort is not guaranteed to produce an immediately optimal solution. Ordinarily, however, it will generate a solution that is not many steps removed from optimality.

The smallest coefficient in Table 4-2A turns out to be c_{C1}—$71 per ton shipped from the Chicago mill to warehouse 1. Accordingly, we attempt to make the entry in the box marked x_{C1} as large as possible. Looking down the column controlling Chicago's capacity, an upper limit of 20 thousand tons is observed for this one allocation. Scanning across the row for warehouse 1, we find the still lower limit of 12 thousand tons and place this as the first basis entry in Table 4-2B. Continuing to fill out the table in this way, we find that the basis entry is at each step governed by either a row total (a requirements equation) or a column total (a capacity limit). The remaining six boxes are, in turn, x_{A4}, x_{C2}, x_{B2}, x_{B3}, x_{A3}, and x_{A5}. The cost of the initial allocation shown in Table 4-2B amounts to $6,577 thousand per week, and the entire total of 14 thousand tons of unused capacity is concentrated upon the Allentown mill.

Before proceeding any further with the simplex calculations, we shall find it of some interest to look ahead and to make an estimate of the maximum gains that could conceivably be derived from any changes in this initial plan. One way to set an upper bound upon these gains is to compare the figure of $6,577 thousand with the total that would be needed if there were enough excess capacity in the system so that each warehouse could be supplied from the point with lowest incremental costs. [This amounts to ignoring the mill capacity limits, restrictions (4-6) to (4-8).] Note that, despite excess capacity in the system as a whole, the resulting allocation plan is a completely infeasible one (Table 4-3). Even with the excess capacity at Allentown, both Birmingham and Chicago would be hopelessly saturated with work.

Total operating costs for this unlimited capacity case would come to $6,386 thousand per week—a reduction of $191 thousand from the initial basic feasible allocation plan: $6,577 thousand.

TABLE 4-3. AJAX STEEL SHIPPING PROBLEM,
UNLIMITED CAPACITY CALCULATION

	Mill			Total requirements, thousands of tons
	Allentown	Birmingham	Chicago	
Warehouse 1	73⌋	95⌋	71⌋ 12	12
Warehouse 2	90⌋	89⌋	82⌋ 21	21
Warehouse 3	97⌋	93⌋ 32	100⌋	32
Warehouse 4	76⌋ 11	94⌋	91⌋	11
Warehouse 5 (excess capacity)	0⌋	0⌋	0⌋	
Total allocations, thousands of tons	11	32	33	
Total capacity, thousands of tons	50	20	20	

$$\sum_j c_j x_j = 76(11) + 93(32) + 71(12) + 82(21) = \$6{,}386 \text{ thousand per week}$$

The reduction of $191 thousand represents an immediate upper bound upon the possible gains that might accrue from reshuffling the initial allocations of mill capacity. The actual gains to be derived through the simplex procedure will necessarily fall short of this limit. If the economic analyst is pressed for a quick answer, this limit provides him with some notion of the maximum penalties that the company might suffer by failing to go through with the formal optimization.

A steel distribution problem (implicit prices)

Assuming that the analyst is not so pressed for time that the simplex calculation is an impractical one, the next move must be to calculate implicit prices and to perform an optimality check upon the initial basic feasible solution shown in Table 4-2B. Just as in all other applications of the simplex method, the economic interpretation of these prices is that they measure either the incremental cost associated with a requirement equation or the incremental cost associated with an availability limit.

Numerically, these prices are found by assigning them in such a way that the implicit worth of each basis activity will just equal the unit payoff coefficient for that activity—here the cost factors c_{C1}, c_{B2}, etc. (For distinction, the implicit prices for the four row-sum requirements will be denoted by u_1, u_2, u_3, and u_4. Similarly, the implicit prices connected with the three column-sum availability totals will be known as u_A, u_B, and u_C—one for each of the three sources of production.)   Activity $C1$, for example, is in the basis (see Table 4-4A).   This means that the implicit worth of mill capacity at Chicago together with the implicit cost of satisfying the requirements of warehouse 1 will have to equal the direct cost of shipments from the Chicago mill to warehouse 1:

$$u_C + u_1 = c_{C1}$$

Within each of the other basis entry boxes, Table 4-4A contains a similar equation—altogether seven simultaneous equations to be solved for the seven implicit prices.   In order to solve this system, we begin with the lower left-hand corner box (the slack activity $A5$) and observe that u_A must equal zero—a highly plausible result in view of the excess capacity at the Allentown mill.   Any addition to the capacity available at Allentown would only bring about an increase in the level of the zero-cost slack activity, $A5$.

Knowing the value of u_A and knowing that boxes $A3$ and $A4$ contain basis entries, we can easily see what u_3 and u_4 must be: $97 and $76 per ton, respectively (see Table 4-4B).   The implicit price u_3 reflects the fact that, with this basis, a one-ton increase in the level of requirements at warehouse 3 will result in an increase in the level of x_{A3} and a decrease in that of x_{A5}—a net cost rise of $97.   A similar argument is applicable to u_4.

The Transportation Model **55**

TABLE 4-4A. AJAX STEEL SHIPPING PROBLEM; IMPLICIT PRICES

	Mill			Implicit cost of warehouse requirements, dollars per ton
	Allentown	Birmingham	Chicago	
Warehouse 1	73|	95|	71| $u_C + u_1 = c_{C1}$	u_1
Warehouse 2	90|	89| $u_B + u_2 = c_{B2}$	82| $u_C + u_2 = c_{C2}$	u_2
Warehouse 3	97| $u_A + u_3 = c_{A3}$	93| $u_B + u_3 = c_{B3}$	100|	u_3
Warehouse 4	76| $u_A + u_4 = c_{A4}$	94|	91|	u_4
Warehouse 5	0| $u_A = c_{A5}$	0|	0|	
Implicit worth of mill capacity, dollars per ton	u_A	u_B	u_C	

TABLE 4-4B. AJAX STEEL SHIPPING PROBLEM; IMPLICIT PRICES

	Mill			Implicit cost of warehouse requirements, dollars per ton
	Allentown	Birmingham	Chicago	
Warehouse 1	73| ⌐82	95| ⌐78	71| $u_C + u_1 = 71$ ⌐71	82
Warehouse 2	90| ⌐93	89| $u_B + u_2 = 89$ ⌐89	82| $u_C + u_2 = 82$ ⌐82	93
Warehouse 3	97| $u_A + u_3 = 97$ ⌐97	93| $u_B + u_3 = 93$ ⌐93	100| ⌐86	97
Warehouse 4	76| $u_A + u_4 = 76$ ⌐76	94| ⌐72	91| ⌐65	76
Warehouse 5	0| $u_A = 0$ ⌐0	0| ⌐−4	0| ⌐−11	
Implicit worth of mill capacity, dollars per ton	0	−4	−11	

To read off the remaining implicit prices, we continue to scan the array of implicit price equations. Whenever we come to a basis entry for which one of the implicit prices is known, the other can be determined by direct subtraction. Thus, knowing that activity $B3$ is in the basis, we have:

$$u_B = 93 - u_3 = -4$$

Why is there a negative value for the incremental worth of mill B's capacity? Because an increase in the capability of this plant would be utilized by increasing the level of x_{B3}, decreasing that of x_{A3}, and increasing x_{A5}—a net *reduction* in over-all costs of $4 per ton of additional capacity. All this information is summarized by the single number u_B.

Proceeding to fill out Table 4-4B, we determine the remaining implicit values in the following sequence:

$$u_2 = 89 - u_B = 93$$
$$u_C = 82 - u_2 = -11$$
$$u_1 = 71 - u_C = 82$$

Table 4-4B lists not only the complete set of implicit prices u_i but also the opportunity cost of each activity, z_j (see the lower right-hand corner of each box). For each activity within the basis, z_j is, of course, equal to the unit cost coefficient c_j. Implicit prices were calculated in such a way as to bring about this equality. Thus, z_{C1} is the opportunity cost of using Chicago's capacity for shipments to warehouse 1; this quantity of $71 per ton equals the incremental value of satisfying requirements at warehouse 1 ($82 per ton) less the incremental value of Chicago's capacity ($11 per ton).

An equality between opportunity costs and direct costs will not be characteristic of all possible activities. It is a necessary condition only for those within the basis. For example, the opportunity cost of shipments from Birmingham to warehouse 1, z_{B1}, is substantially smaller than c_{B1}, or $95, the direct cost of shipments between these two points:

$$z_{B1} = u_B + u_1 = -4 + 82 = \$78 \text{ per ton}$$

This abstract-looking calculation indicates a perfectly commonsensical result. Each unit of activity $B2$ produces something worth \$78 net, but costs \$95. Nothing is to be gained by introducing it into the basis. Just as in the profit-maximizing examples discussed previously, everything hinges upon the sign of the difference between the payoff coefficient and the opportunity cost of the activity. Here in our cost-minimizing problem, we want to introduce an activity only if the difference $z_j - c_j$ is positive. According to Table 4-4B, the initial tableau contains only two boxes for which z_j exceeds c_j: boxes $A1$ and $A2$. Since $z_{A1} - c_{A1}$ is larger than $z_{A2} - c_{A2}$, the one to be introduced into the basis will be activity $A1$. Each ton allocated in this way will reduce over-all costs by (\$82 − \$73) = \$9. If, in the new basis, x_{A1} is represented as θ tons, the net cost reduction will amount to \$9 (θ). The next step in the simplex routine, then, is to see what adjustments must be made in the other basis variables so as to allow θ, and thereby the net cost reduction, to grow as large as possible. As in the preceding chapter, the adjusted values of the unknowns will be indicated by x_j' to distinguish them from the initial values x_j.

A steel distribution problem (adjustments in initial allocations)

Table 4-5A reveals the pattern that these adjustments must follow: First, if x_{A1}' is to take on the value of θ, then in order for the first warehouse's requirements to be satisfied, x_{C1}' must equal $12 - \theta$. In other words, the adjustment per unit of the new activity, the quantity termed Δ_j in the preceding chapter, must be -1. Similarly, to preserve the column-sum restriction for Chicago's capacity, it in turn becomes necessary for the unknown x_{C2}' to take on the value of $8 + \theta$. The unit change, Δ_{C2}, equals $+1$ in this instance, and so on.

To find out how large θ can be made, we shall have to search for the bottleneck basis variable—the one that will first be driven down to a value of zero and removed from the basis. To do this, we check through those activities for which Δ_j is negative and

TABLE 4-5A. AJAX STEEL SHIPPING PROBLEM, ADJUSTMENTS IN INITIAL ALLOCATIONS

	Mill			Total requirements, thousands of tons
	Allentown	Birmingham	Chicago	
Warehouse 1	$\boxed{73}$ $x'_{A1} = \theta$	$\boxed{95}$	$\boxed{71}$ $x'_{C1} = 12 - \theta$	12
Warehouse 2	$\boxed{90}$	$\boxed{89}$ $x'_{B2} = 13 - \theta$	$\boxed{82}$ $x'_{C2} = 8 + \theta$	21
Warehouse 3	$\boxed{97}$ $x'_{A3} = 25 - \theta$	$\boxed{93}$ $x'_{B3} = 7 + \theta$	$\boxed{100}$	32
Warehouse 4	$\boxed{76}$ $x'_{A4} = 11 + 0$	$\boxed{94}$	$\boxed{91}$	11
Warehouse 5 (excess capacity)	$\boxed{0}$ $x'_{A5} = 14 + 0$	$\boxed{0}$	$\boxed{0}$	
Total capacity, thousands of tons	50	20	20	

TABLE 4-5B. AJAX STEEL SHIPPING PROBLEM, ADJUSTED ALLOCATIONS, SECOND TABLEAU

	Mill			Total requirements, thousands of tons	Implicit cost of warehouse requirements, dollars per ton
	Allentown	Birmingham	Chicago		
Warehouse 1	$\boxed{73}$ 12	$\boxed{95}$	$\boxed{71}$	12	$u_1 = 73$
Warehouse 2	$\boxed{90}$	$\boxed{89}$ 1	$\boxed{82}$ 20	21	$u_2 = 93$
Warehouse 3	$\boxed{97}$ 13	$\boxed{93}$ 19	$\boxed{100}$	32	$u_3 = 97$
Warehouse 4	$\boxed{76}$ 11	$\boxed{94}$	$\boxed{91}$	11	$u_4 = 76$
Warehouse 5 (excess capacity)	$\boxed{0}$ 14	$\boxed{0}$	$\boxed{0}$		
Total capacity, thousands of tons	50	20	20		
Implicit worth of mill capacity, dollars per ton	$u_A = 0$	$u_B = -4$	$u_C = -11$		

$$\sum_j c_j x_j = \$6{,}469 \text{ thousand per week}$$

single out that one for which the ratio $x_j/-\Delta_j$ is smallest.   This ratio immediately yields the value of θ in our new solution.   In Table 4-5A, there turn out to be three basis entries for which Δ_j is negative—in all three cases, equal to -1.   The ratio $x_j/-\Delta_j$ here simplifies to x_j itself.   The smallest of the three quantities x_{A3}, x_{B2}, and x_{C1} is, of course, x_{C1} with a value of 12.

This ratio test not only reveals that activity $C1$ is the one to be eliminated from the basis, but also provides us with the value of θ, the level of the new activity in the basis, x'_{A1}.   Table 4-5B contains the numerical values of all basis variables after the indicated adjustments have been carried out.   The total cost of executing this new plan of operations is $6,469 thousand per week—a reduction of $108 thousand from the initial level of $6,577 thousand.   As a numerical check, it can be verified that the magnitude of this reduction equals

$$(z_j - c_j)\theta = (82 - 73)12 = \$108 \text{ thousand}$$

Table 4-5B also provides the starting point for our next iteration—first a determination of implicit prices and of opportunity costs and then the adjustments to be made in each of the basis variables.

Implicit prices are again obtained by imputing them in such a way that the implicit worth of each activity within the basis is exactly equal to the direct cost of that activity.   Thus,

$$u_A = c_{A5} = 0$$
$$u_3 = c_{A3} - u_A = 97 - 0 = 97$$
$$u_B = c_{B3} - u_3 = 93 - 97 = -4$$
. . . .

All seven implicit prices u_i appear in Table 4-5B.   Only one positive difference, $z_j - c_j$, shows up: $z_{A2} - c_{A2} = 93 - 90 = \$3$ per ton shipped from Allentown to warehouse 2.

Accordingly, the quantity θ is entered in the $A2$ box, and the values of all basis variables are adjusted so as to satisfy the row- and column-sum restrictions (see Table 4-6).   The bottleneck activity now turns out to be x_{B2}.   The maximum value that can be assigned to θ is the almost negligible quantity of 1 thousand tons.   Alas, not all moves in the simplex process lead to dramatic improvements!

TABLE 4-6. AJAX STEEL SHIPPING PROBLEM;
ADJUSTMENTS IN SECOND TABLEAU

	Mill			Total requirements, thousands of tons
	Allentown	Birmingham	Chicago	
Warehouse 1	73 12	95	71	12
Warehouse 2	90 θ	89 $1 - \theta$	82 20	21
Warehouse 3	97 $13 - \theta$	93 $19 + \theta$	100	32
Warehouse 4	76 11	94	91	11
Warehouse 5 (excess capacity)	0 14	0	0	
Total capacity, thousands of tons	50	20	20	

The third basic feasible solution, like its predecessor, is formed according to the definition:

$$x'_j = x_j + \Delta_j \, \theta \qquad (3\text{-}12)$$

The new solution and the new implicit prices are all included in Table 4-7.   None of the differences $z_j - c_j$ are positive, so we know that this is an optimal solution.   No matter what further reshuffling of allocations is done, total costs cannot be reduced below the level of $6,466 thousand per week—$111 thousand beneath the starting point of $6,577 thousand.[1]   This saving is still considerably short of the amount previously calculated for

---

[1] It is of some interest that activity $C1$ with the lowest unit cost does not appear in the optimal basis.   What this means is that, although it appears cheap to supply warehouse 1 out of the Chicago mill, it is still better to pay a penalty at that point in order to use the capacity elsewhere.

the unlimited capacity case. Were mill capacities unlimited, there would be no obstacle in the way of supplying each warehouse from the least expensive source of supply. Incremental shipping and production costs could be lowered to a total of $6,386 thousand—a reduction of $191 thousand.

TABLE 4-7. AJAX STEEL SHIPPING PROBLEM; OPTIMAL ALLOCATIONS; THIRD TABLEAU

	Mill			Total requirements, thousands of tons	Implicit cost of warehouse requirements, dollars per ton
	Allentown	Birmingham	Chicago		
Warehouse 1	73 12	95	71	12	73
Warehouse 2	90 1	89	82 20	21	90
Warehouse 3	97 12	93 20	100	32	97
Warehouse 4	76 11	94	91	11	76
Warehouse 5 (excess capacity)	0 14	0	0		
Total capacity, thousands of tons	50	20	20		
Implicit worth of mill capacity, dollars per ton	0	−4	−8		

$$\sum_j c_j x_j = \$6,466 \text{ thousand per week}$$

When mill capacities are limited, however, there can be no hope of achieving a reduction of as much as $191 thousand. No amount of reshuffling of steel allocations can obscure the very real fact that the Ajax Company is short of productive capacity in the Birmingham and the Chicago areas and that it has a surplus in Allentown. Linear programming can only partially offset this geographical imbalance.

Company-wide policy implications

Top management people will ordinarily display far less interest in the technical details of this kind of model than in the underlying assumptions. As far as the Ajax Company is concerned, one obvious question that is bound to arise is in connection with surplus capacity. The transportation model has come up with the recommendation that all excess capacity be concentrated at a single point—the Allentown mill, the largest and possibly the oldest productive unit in the company. The Allentown superintendent is almost certain to view this result with a jaundiced eye and, indeed, to become an avowed enemy of any subsequent attempts at linear programming within his domain. For precisely the opposite and equally wrong reasons, the superintendents at Birmingham and Chicago are likely to become enthusiastic supporters of such analyses.

The Allentown superintendent surely has some justice on his side. Just because his is the high-cost mill, the linear programming model will tend to concentrate any fluctuations in over-all production upon the one plant. Community relations are bound to suffer from such a policy, and the union local will come to feel that it is a victim of deliberate persecution on the part of the entire company. It is a safe bet that the top management at Ajax will lend an attentive ear to these complaints.

Economic analysts are only human, and the most tempting course for a human being subjected to the Allentown criticism is to become obstinate and to insist that the solution is an impeccably optimal one. There is no compelling reason, however, for the analyst to succumb to this temptation. Instead he is well within his rights to say something along the following lines: "At the time the transportation matrix was set up, nobody bothered to specify how excess capacity was to be allocated, and I made the incorrect assumption that this didn't make any difference. Apparently it does, and I will be happy to recalculate my allocations if you can tell me how you would like the 14 thousand tons of excess capacity distributed among the three mills. The previous work, however, is by no means completely useless. At this point I can tell you how much it will cost to reduce Allentown's unemployment and to increase unemployment at either Birmingham or Chicago. The implicit prices indicate that your work-spreading policy is going to cost you $4 for each ton of work diverted from Birmingham to Allentown and that it will cost you $8 for each ton taken from Chicago (see Table 4-7). Now that you know these figures, you are certainly in a better position than ever before to decide on how far you want to move in the direction of helping Allentown."

Here once again, the benefits derived from economic analysis have little to do with the details of the optimal operating plan, but rather with the sensitivity tests that become possible—tests that evaluate the cost of arbitrarily imposed policies. As so often happens, it may turn out that raising questions is a more valuable activity than providing answers.

Production scheduling and inventory storage

The versatility of the transportation model can best be appreciated through a second application—one that has nothing to do with transportation in a geographical sense—the problem of production scheduling over time within a seasonal industry. The Apollo Antifreeze Company, for example, is continually plagued by the fact that automobile owners purchase far more of its product during the fall and winter months than they do during the spring or summer. (Export sales to the Southern Hemisphere have as yet attained only modest proportions.) Quarterly sales are estimated at the following levels:

Spring quarter	90
Summer quarter	160
Fall quarter	490
Winter quarter	360
Annual total	1,100 thousand gallons

Two sources of supply are open to Apollo—its own plant with a capacity of 300 thousand gallons per quarter and an outside supplier who is willing to make a contract for fall and winter delivery in whatever quantities are needed to supplement Apollo's own output. With the onset of spring, the company is faced with its usual policy problem: How much shall it produce and store during the slow months, and to what extent shall it rely upon the outside supplier? A related problem also arises—this of a longer-range nature: How much could be saved if the company were to construct additional productive capacity of its own?

All these questions involve cost estimates: the cost of outside purchase, of home production, and of storage. The easiest such estimate to make is the one related to an outside-purchase contract. Any money spent through this contract is a clear out-of-pocket expense to the Apollo Company. For purposes of this example, we shall assume that there are no economies involved in large-scale purchases and that the unit price paid for any material is $2 per gallon.

The incremental cost of producing antifreeze in Apollo's own plant ($1.50 per gallon) will necessarily be a more debatable kind of estimate. Just as in the Ajax Steel case, this $1.50 figure is one that excludes any allowance for fixed costs—costs that are independent of the number of gallons produced by the Apollo Company itself. The only items that properly enter this esti-mate are those costs that can be made to vary in a seasonal manner, e.g., raw materials, power, unskilled labor, and any maintenance that depends upon throughput rather than calendar time. Excluded from this estimate would be all plant overhead items. Plant overhead is an avoidable cost only if we are con-sidering the possibility of closing down the plant indefinitely. Typically, very little overhead can be saved by a purely seasonal shutdown, and it is only this seasonal shutdown that is at issue here. Were an indefinite shutdown under consideration, the plant's overhead costs would become a very relevant item.

To complete the analysis of the Apollo Company's scheduling problem, we need some sort of estimate of the costs of storage—

not only the costs of storage space plus product deterioration[1] but also the implicit worth of the capital that is tied up. The total figure might come out to be $.20 per gallon for each 3 months stored. From the very outset, however, we ought to recognize that the storage cost estimate is subject to a good deal of imprecision and that we shall want to make some sensitivity tests, i.e., to find out what happens if, instead of $.20, a different value is assigned, say, $.15 or $.25 for each quarter of a year.

TABLE 4-8. APOLLO ANTIFREEZE SCHEDULING PROBLEM

	Capacity available in				Outside supplier	Total requirements, thousands of gallons
	Spring quarter	Summer quarter	Fall quarter	Winter quarter		
Sales requirements, spring quarter	1.50⌋ x_{1i}					90
Sales requirements, summer quarter	1.70⌋ x_{12}	1.50⌋ x_{22}				160
Sales requirements, fall quarter	1.90⌋ x_{13}	1.70⌋ x_{23}	1.50⌋ x_{33}		2.00⌋ x_{53}	490
Sales requirements, winter quarter	2.10⌋ x_{14}	1.90⌋ x_{24}	1.70⌋ x_{34}	1.50⌋ x_{44}	2.00⌋ x_{54}	360
Excess capacity	0⌋ x_{15}	0⌋ x_{25}	0⌋ x_{35}	0⌋ x_{45}	0⌋ x_{55}	
Total capacity, thousands of gallons	300	250	300	300	1,000	

The cost factors, together with the requirement and availability forecasts given earlier, can be organized within a tableau (Table 4-8) that is almost identical with the layout for the Ajax transportation problem. The unknown quantities to be entered within each box represent the amount of productive capacity

[1] If, instead of antifreeze, we were considering a seasonal buildup of an item with periodic style changes, e.g., automobiles or washing machines, the cost of obsolescence would also have to be included.

available from one period that is to be allocated toward meeting one or another of the quarterly sales requirements. The entry x_{11}, for example, indicates the number of thousands of gallons produced within the first quarter to be used for covering that season's sales. Similarly, the entry x_{12} indicates the amount to be produced in the first quarter and carried over for use in the second quarter. Entries like x_{21}, x_{31}, etc., are crossed off this table in order to satisfy the very common-sense requirement that we cannot borrow from future capabilities in order to meet current sales commitments.

The column totals within Table 4-8 no longer refer to the amount of productive capacity available at each geographical location, but rather to the amount of capacity available during each of the four seasons: 300 thousand gallons per quarter. (Because of summer vacation shutdowns, only 250 thousand gallons of capacity are indicated for that period.) The fifth-column total governs the total amount of outside purchases available to the Apollo Company and is nominally set at a very high level—a million gallons—to reflect the fact that this source of supply is, to all intents and purposes, an unlimited one. (How would this tableau be altered if there were a third source of supply: second-shift production each quarter at a premium labor cost?)

The first four row totals are used for controlling not the sales requirements of each individual geographical area, but instead the requirements at each of the four points in time. The fifth row, as in the Ajax example, is reserved for the slack variables, the amounts of unused capacity available from each of the five sources of supply.

The cost coefficients shown in the upper left-hand corner of each box indicate the unit costs associated with the respective activity. Thus, c_{11}, the coefficient associated with x_{11}, equals $1.50, the unit cost within the company's own plant. No storage costs are incurred because of the fact that activity 11 refers to the production of antifreeze during the spring quarter for use during that quarter. With activity 12, on the other hand, there are storage costs involved. For each gallon entered

TABLE 4-9. APOLLO ANTIFREEZE SCHEDULING PROBLEM, OPTIMAL ALLOCATIONS

	Capacity available in				Outside supplier	Total requirements, thousands of gallons	Implicit cost of sales requirements, dollars per gallon
	Spring quarter	Summer quarter	Fall quarter	Winter quarter			
Sales requirements, spring quarter	1.50 — 90	✕	✕	✕	✕	90	1.50
Sales requirements, summer quarter	1.70	1.50 — 160	✕	✕	✕	160	1.70
Sales requirements, fall quarter	1.90 — 100	1.70 — 90	1.50 — 300	✕	2.00	490	1.90
Sales requirements, winter quarter	2.10	1.90	1.70	1.50 — 300	2.00 — 60	360	2.00
Excess capacity	0 — 110	0	0	0		940	
Total capacity, thousands of gallons	300	250	300	300	1,000		
Implicit worth of capacity, dollars per gallon	0	−.20	−.40	−.50	0		

within box 12, there is, in addition to the direct costs of production, the $.20 cost of storage for one quarter of a year. This brings the cost coefficient c_{12} to a total of $1.70 per gallon. Similarly, the coefficient c_{13} is associated with an activity implying storage over two quarters of a year and therefore a cost of $1.90.

An optimal solution to Apollo's seasonal scheduling problem is shown in Table 4-9.[1] (There is more than one optimal solution

[1] With this particular kind of scheduling problem, there is a remarkably easy short-cut method for producing optimal solutions directly on the very first iteration. See Selmer Johnson, "Sequential Production Planning over Time at Minimum Cost," *Management Science*, July, 1957.

to this example.   Calculate another one that is equally optimal.)
Several things are worth noting about the optimal plan that is
shown: First, although the peak in demand occurs during the
fall quarter, it does not pay to take delivery until winter of the
supplementary product purchased from outside sources.   As long
as the outside supplier is willing to provide his product at the
same $2 price regardless of whether delivered in the fall or the
winter, it pays to let him, in effect, take over the storage job for
one extra quarter.   Second, the implicit cost of meeting the
peak fall demand is $1.90 a gallon—actually lower than the $2
cost associated with the winter season's demand.   These facts
are surely worth considering when it comes time for the sales
department to negotiate contracts with distributors for delivery
of the packaged antifreeze product.   Other things being the
same, the Apollo Company will be better off by $.10 a gallon if
it can expand its fall sales rather than those during the somewhat
slower winter season.   The implicit costs shown here illustrate
the deceptiveness of judging peak seasonal strains by looking
at the demand pattern only and by ignoring the capacity limitations that confront the company.

Some sensitivity analysis questions

1. How low could the unit costs of storage drop and how high
would they have to rise from the level of $.20 per gallon before
it would pay to alter the solution shown on Table 4-9?

2. Suppose that it is believed unrealistic for the storage costs
to be considered as uniform from one quarter to the next.   To
be specific, Apollo's accounting department calculates that the
cost of carrying inventory from the summer into the peak fall
season is $.35 a gallon but that it is only $.10 a gallon between
each of the other quarters.   By how much, if at all, would it
then be desirable to change the inventory-buildup plan shown
in Table 4-9?

3. How much would the company be able to save if it shifted
the summer vacation shutdown into the spring season?   Justify
your answer by means of implicit prices.

4. Use the implicit prices shown in Table 4-9 to calculate how much Apollo would save each year if it enlarged its plant so as to provide 120 thousand gallons of additional annual capacity, i.e., 30 thousand gallons per quarter. You may assume that the unit production cost of $1.50 a gallon would be unaffected by the expansion program.

5. In setting up this year's production and outside procurement plan, would there be any advantage in also taking account of next year's demands and plant capacity availabilities?

6. What benefit will there be to the Apollo Company if it is able to wait until the end of the summer season before it specifies the exact quantities to be delivered during the winter season by the outside supplier?

APPENDIX TO CHAPTER 4

Note: If the reader is not particularly interested in details, he may want to skip this appendix.

Some general characteristics of "transportation" models

From the standpoint of numerical analysis, the striking thing that makes a transportation model so easy to solve is that at each step the system of simultaneous equations can always be handled in a "triangular" or one-at-a-time fashion. No matter what activities happen to make up the basis, it is possible to use one of the equations to solve for one unknown x_j, then to insert this value into a second equation to solve for a second x_j, and so on. This characteristic holds true not only for the activity levels x_j but also for the implicit prices u_i and for the unit changes in activity levels Δ_j. A formal proof follows:

Suppose that in the Ajax Steel example the total number of mills owned by the company is denoted by M and the total number of warehouses by W. The array for this enterprise will then contain M columns and $W + 1$ rows. (Note that an extra row is needed for the M individual slack activities.) In

Table 4-2A, for example, $M = 3$ and $W = 4$. The total number of rows in the array, however, equals 5.

Without loss of generality, we may suppose that $W \geq M$. In addition, we know that there will always be $M + W$ equations associated with such an array—hence, exactly $M + W$ activities in the basis.

The one-at-a-time theorem is proved by showing that its denial leads to a contradiction. To deny the theorem is to assert that, in scanning the array in order to evaluate the activity levels x_j, we shall be unable to locate a single row or column containing just one unknown activity level. This means that there must be at least two basis activities in each of the $W + 1$ rows—hence, at least $2W + 2$ basis activities altogether—a number clearly larger than $W + M$.

Here we have the desired contradiction, or rather a contradiction as far as the first unknown is concerned. To prove that the same reasoning applies to the next one, we observe that our previous calculation has merely reduced the original transportation array to a second array—an array with one less row (or column) and one less activity level to be determined. The same argument now applies to prove that, as long as any unknowns remain, we shall always be able to locate some row (or column) within the array that contains no more than one unknown.

Integer solutions

Not only does this one-at-a-time feature make the transportation problem so amenable to hand calculation, but also this remarkable feature guarantees that every basic feasible solution will consist of integer numbers, not of fractions. That is to say, if the requirements and availabilities are both stated to the nearest thousand tons, then the activity levels x_j will also come out to the nearest thousand tons. The integral nature of the solution is not a very important matter when dealing with such an obviously divisible item as one thousand tons of steel, but it does make a difference when considering such indivisible units as an airplane or a tankship. There it would be a very awkward thing indeed if the linear programming solution required the forward half to be dispatched to a different destination from the after half. Fortunately, if the case fits into the transportation form, it can be guaranteed that this particular possibility will not arise.

Why is it that this possibility will not arise? Because whenever a whole number is either added to or subtracted from another, the result is itself a whole number. The entire process of solving for activity levels consists of adding and subtracting whole numbers.

The problem of degeneracy

Suppose that by some accident the Ajax Steel Company had estimated its requirements for the second warehouse as 20 thousand tons instead of 21 thousand. If the reader goes back to Table 4-7, he will notice that the basis variable x_{A2} would, as a result of this change, drop to zero. Such an accident—one in which the m constraint equations can be satisfied with fewer than m activities at positive levels—is what is technically known as degeneracy. Why should anyone worry about this peculiar kind of occurrence? After all, it took only a minor correction in the optimal tableau to deal with it. Why bother any further?

The reason for concern with degeneracy has much less to do with the activity levels appearing in the final tableau than with the implicit prices. If we have only six activities at positive levels, which seven equations are to be used for calculating the seven implicit prices? And if we cannot find these implicit prices, how are we ever to determine whether or not this is an optimal solution? It is in order to cope with this question that research workers have been stimulated into devising special computational methods.

Among these methods, the most general-purpose one is that devised by Charnes.[1] This is one that will handle degeneracy

---

[1] A. Charnes, "Optimality and Degeneracy in Linear Programming," *Econometrica*, April, 1952, pp. 160–170.

in any linear programming problem, regardless of whether or not it has a specialized structure. Charnes's approach is, however, a fairly cumbersome thing to use, so instead we shall confine the discussion to a method developed by A. Orden for dealing with a very special kind of linear programming structure, namely, one of the transportation type.[1]

Orden's method is one that would have been embraced as metaphysical by Bishop Berkeley. Orden says, in effect, that we are to pretend that the total requirements due at warehouse 2 are to be considered not as 20 thousand tons weekly, but rather as 20 thousand plus a very small positive number—"the ghost of a departed quantity"—and that we are to refer to this quantity as ϵ, the Greek letter epsilon. In fact, each of the row requirements is to be augmented by this very small amount, and one of the columns by 5ϵ. Table 4-10 indicates not only these alterations but also the corresponding adjustments to be made in each of the basis variables. By changing the original row and column totals in this way, the degeneracy problem can be sidestepped altogether. Instead of six unknowns, seven basis entries now appear at positive levels—always with the understanding that epsilon, though a vanishingly small quantity, is still a positive number. Orden's technique amounts to ensuring that no *partial* algebraic sum of the row totals will ever equal a partial algebraic sum of the column totals.

No formal proof will be given here, but the theorem can be put this way: Take any small number you please. Add it to each of the row requirements in your original problem, and if there are $W + 1$ rows altogether, add $(W + 1)\epsilon$ to one of the column totals. Solve using the simplex method. Degeneracy will never arise during the course of your iterations, and furthermore, once you have found an optimal solution, it will still be optimal even after you have rounded away the epsilon quantities

[1] Orden's theorem is presented within a paper by G. B. Dantzig, "Application of the Simplex Method to a Transportation Problem," in T. C. Koopmans (ed.), *Activity Analysis of Production and Allocation*, John Wiley & Sons, Inc., New York, 1951.

to arrive back at the original problem. Two qualifications to this way of phrasing Orden's theorem: (1) If there are more column- than row-sum restrictions, add epsilon to each of the column totals rather than to the rows. If the Ajax Company, for example, had four warehouses but owned six steel mills, the epsilon quantity would then be added to each of the mill capacity totals.   (2) In numerical calculations, it is sometimes convenient to add an honest-to-goodness number such as 0.01 thousand tons

**TABLE 4-10. AJAX STEEL SHIPPING PROBLEM;
EPSILON ADJUSTMENTS**

	Mill			Total requirements, thousands of tons
	Allentown	Birmingham	Chicago	
Warehouse 1	73 $12 + \epsilon$	95	71	$12 + \epsilon$
Warehouse 2	90 ϵ	89	82 20	$20 + \epsilon$
Warehouse 3	97 $12 + \epsilon$	93 20	100	$32 + \epsilon$
Warehouse 4	76 $11 + \epsilon$	94	91	$11 + \epsilon$
Warehouse 5 (excess capacity)	0 $15 + \epsilon$	0	0	
Total capacity, thousands of tons	$50 + 5\epsilon$	20	20	

to each of the row totals in place of the symbol epsilon. Any number will do—provided that it is smaller than $d/[2(W + 1)]$. ($W + 1$ here represents the total number of rows in the array, and d is the least significant digit in the row or column totals.) For the Ajax Steel tableau, $d/[2(W + 1)] = 1/[2(5)]$. Therefore, any number smaller than $\frac{1}{10}$ will eliminate the possibility of degeneracy.

EXERCISES

4-1. Every three months, an armed services petroleum procurement agency takes in bids for the supply of jet fuel from the major refining centers on the Gulf Coast, the East Coast, and the West Coast.[1] Bids are received in the following amounts from each of the three refining areas:

Gulf Coast	$4.00 per barrel up to a maximum of 13 million barrels
East Coast	$5.00 per barrel up to a maximum of 10 million barrels
West Coast	$5.50 per barrel up to a maximum of 8 million barrels

In addition, there are a group of Gulf Coast refiners who are willing to supply quantities of jet fuel at a $5 price up to a maximum of 4 million barrels.

Consumption requirements for the three-month period are forecast as follows:

Far West	10.3
Middle West	7.1
South	6.2
Northeast	9.1
Total requirements	32.7 million barrels

Transportation costs (per barrel) between each of the refining centers and the consuming areas are:

[1] Walter Jacobs has referred to an actual problem of this type in "Military Applications of Linear Programming," *Proceedings of the Second Symposium in Linear Programming*, DCS/Comptroller, U.S. Air Force, Washington, D.C., January, 1955.

From	To			
	Far West	Middle West	South	Northeast
Gulf Coast.............	$1.30	$ .90	$ .40	$1.10
East Coast.............	2.00	1.00	.70	.20
West Coast.............	.30	1.20	1.50	2.50

The agency is directed by law to award its bids so as to minimize the over-all cost of meeting jet fuel requirements in the Air Force and Navy consuming areas.   Does the agency necessarily reject the high price of $5.50 bid by the West Coast refiners?   Which bids ought to be accepted?

4-2. The Minerva Sewing Machine Company is engaged in phasing out the manufacture of one of its subassemblies within the United States and is shifting production to its European plant.   The subassembly will be needed for final assembly within the United States and the European plant in the following quantities:

Quarter	Thousands of subassemblies required	
	United States plant	European plant
January–March........	20	10
April–June...........	50	15
July–September........	50	25

The United States plant has a capacity of 50 thousand subassemblies per quarter but is scheduled to shut down at the end of March.   The European facility will build up its capacity from 20 thousand in the first quarter to 40 thousand in the second and to 80 thousand in the third quarter.

The incremental costs of production in the United States are $15 per unit, and only $10 in Europe.   Shipping costs plus import duties amount to $2 per unit sent from the United States to Europe and $3 per unit sent in the reverse direction. Inventory holding costs are estimated at $1.30 per quarter of a year for each unit held.

If the object is to satisfy the delivery requirements at minimum total cost, how much should be produced at the two locations within each time period? How much should be shipped in each direction? How much production ought to go into inventory? What are some of the benefits that the Minerva Company might hope to gain if it kept the United States plant in operation during the April to June quarter?

4-3. Five graduate seminars in Industrial Administration are to be scheduled so as not to conflict with one another. One seminar is to meet on each weekday afternoon.

Because of other class schedules and also outside work commitments, certain students will be forced to drop out of these seminars. The following array indicates, for example, that if Industrial Administration 141 is held on Monday afternoons, three students will be unable to take the course, and that if it is held on Tuesdays, ten students will be unable to take it.

Day	I.A. 141	I.A. 142	I.A. 143	I.A. 144	I.A. 145
Monday............	3	2	3	10	9
Tuesday...........	10	5	8	10	2
Wednesday........	1	3	10	2	4
Thursday..........	6	10	10	5	2
Friday............	8	6	5	6	10

Use a transportation model to schedule dates for these seminars in such a way as to minimize the total number of people forced to drop out.

Hint. Before attempting to solve the problem, be sure to read the Appendix to this chapter.

CHAPTER FIVE

MARKETING

Introduction

In most of the cases discussed up to this point, we have proceeded as though exclusively preoccupied with the kinds of decisions to be made within the manufacturing and the transportation departments of a business enterprise. Only a few attempts were made to link these decisions to those of a sales or a marketing department; and these attempts occurred in the course of interpreting implicit prices derived from the simplex calculation, e.g., the amount the oil refiner could afford to spend on advertising in order to bring in an additional barrel of gasoline sales. Typically, the problem phrased has been one of meeting a fixed sales requirement at minimum cost. Such problems, no doubt, are the easiest to formulate and to solve. They do not, however, furnish a direct answer to one of the more exacting kinds of questions faced by the typical business firm: the question of what products it ought to attempt to sell and how much effort it ought to devote to selling them.

On the surface, there is no reason for this lack of symmetry between the treatment of selling decisions and of production decisions. From the viewpoint of formal economic logic, there is little difference between the problem of choosing a product mix so as to maximize profits and the problem of choosing an

input mix so as to minimize costs. The difference between an
analysis of marketing and an analysis of production decisions
lies almost exclusively in the extent of our ignorance concerning
effort-response relationships in marketing. In most business
enterprises, an appallingly small amount is understood concerning
the reaction of sales volume to price and nonprice competition.[1]
A marketing manager will always be able to recollect instances
in which a product was repackaged, its price tag marked up,
and customers swarmed in to acquire the item. The fact that
more was purchased at the higher price certainly poses a difficult
problem to the analyst who is determined to read perfect ration-
ality into every action. And in his grumpy way, the analyst is
likely to remind the sales manager that not all price markups
have led to such a happy conclusion.

In the presence of such widespread lack of knowledge, there
are two obvious lines for the quantitative-minded to take: One
is to assume that both the price received and the sales requirements are completely beyond the control of the business enterprise and that the only problem is one of supplying these requirements at minimum total cost. (This is the approach that we
took, for example, in the transportation models of the preceding
chapter.) The other extreme is for the analyst to suppose that
the enterprise can sell as much or as little as it pleases of any
product at the going market price. This was the marketing
assumption in the brass mill case and also in the farm family
example (exercise 3-5). This other extreme coincides with what
the economist traditionally terms "perfect competition."[2]

---

[1] Some encouraging quantitative work has begun to appear in this area.
See M. L. Vidale and H. B. Wolfe, "Sales Response to Advertising," *Operations Research*, June, 1957.

[2] When an economist uses the word "perfect" to describe the workings of
a market, he is not thereby passing a value judgment on the workings of
that particular sector. He is using the phrase "perfect competition" in
precisely the same sense as the physicist uses the term "ideal gas" or "perfectly elastic body"—to indicate that, in order to make analysis possible,
he has neglected many of the interesting phenomena that are to be found in
actual markets. In his quest for simplicity, the economist often argues
that each enterprise competing within a given industry acts *as though* it
could sell an unlimited quantity of any one of its products without affecting

Whatever are the merits of the perfect competition hypothesis in public policy discussions, there are few large business enterprises in which this seems at all helpful in arriving at internal decisions. Almost inevitably some elements of imperfect competition will have to be recognized. In general, the firm cannot sell as much or as little of each product as it pleases without affecting either the price received or any of its future market opportunities. In abandoning the perfect competition model, however, one would be mistaken in rushing back to the other extreme that is so easy to analyze: the assumption that the enterprise is powerless to influence the quantity sold.

This chapter is concerned with one type of model that seems appropriate when we are no longer satisfied with the two obvious extremes: on the one hand, perfect competition, and on the other, zero control over the quantities sold. The situation to be studied will be one in which the greater the quantity sold, the lower will be the incremental return.[1] In accordance with well-known principles of theoretical economics, the case will be one in which someone else has already completed the really difficult job—that of determining a numerical relationship between the price and the quantity response.

A newsprint marketing problem (introduction)

The Parnassus Paper and Pulp Company is planning to establish a newsprint mill at an inland point, town A. The company's

---

the market price. The economist recognizes that this is a fiction but argues that the perfect competition model is, in many respects, a serviceable guide through the maze of public policy issues in economics. Milton Friedman has argued convincingly in defense of this point. See "The Methodology of Positive Economics," *Essays in Positive Economics*, University of Chicago Press, Chicago, 1953.

[1] Throughout this volume, we shall neglect an even more significant intermediate case, oligopoly, a situation in which there are so few sellers in direct competition that each must frame his actions so as to take account of the others' reactions. This situation results in Sherlock Holmes's trying to guess what Dr. Moriarity will guess that Sherlock Holmes will guess. . . . For more on this intriguing area, see M. Shubik, *Strategy and Market Structure*, John Wiley & Sons, Inc., New York, 1959.

immediate problem is one of deciding in which areas it ought to attempt to obtain long-range contracts for the sale of the various grades of newsprint that the mill is capable of producing. These marketing plans must, of course, be fitted in with the production capacity planned for the new mill.

For purposes of this example, it will be assumed that there are only two grades of product: wide rolls and narrow ones. The primary competition facing the new mill will come from imports shipped into the region by way of the coastal town at port D (Figure 5-1). The four logical zones within which the mill

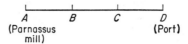

$$
\begin{array}{cccc}
A & B & C & D \\
\text{(Parnassus} & & & \text{(Port)} \\
\text{mill)} & & &
\end{array}
$$

Fig. 5-1. Geographical relationships for newsprint problem.

might sell its products are town A itself plus towns B, C, and D. The unknowns of this marketing problem are x_{WA}, x_{WB}, x_{WC}, and x_{WD}—thousands of tons of wide rolls shipped annually into towns A, B, C, and D—and x_{NA}, x_{NB}, x_{NC}, and x_{ND}—the respective volumes of narrow-width tonnage.

The mill is rated as capable of producing 125 thousand tons annually of wide rolls or 100 thousand tons of narrow rolls. To keep within the mill's capacity, the first restriction that any marketing plan must satisfy is the following:

$$x_{WA} + x_{WB} + x_{WC} + x_{WD} + 1.25(x_{NA} + x_{NB} + x_{NC} + x_{ND})$$
$$\leq 125 \quad (5\text{-}1)$$

After some preliminary survey work, the Parnassus Company estimates that the market potential within each of the four zones is identical: 30 thousand tons per year of the wide product and 20 thousand of the narrow. These potentials impose the following upper limits upon the individual unknowns:

$$
\begin{array}{ll}
x_{WA} \leq 30 & x_{NA} \leq 20 \\
x_{WB} \leq 30 & x_{NB} \leq 20 \\
x_{WC} \leq 30 & x_{NC} \leq 20 \\
x_{WD} \leq 30 & x_{ND} \leq 20
\end{array} \quad (5\text{-}2)
$$

Contract prices for delivery within the four areas are conventionally established as the price at port D plus the freight inland from that point.[1] Parnassus wants to avoid precipitating a price war and, accordingly, has decided to follow this general practice, despite the fact that this will mean a higher mill netback[2] on sales to its nearby customers and a lower netback on the more

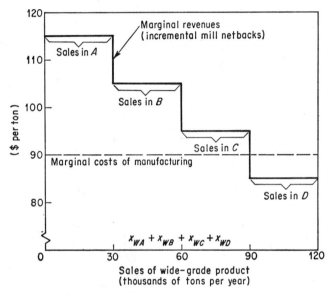

Fig. 5-2. Marginal revenues on wide-grade product.

distant ones.   In the basing-point literature, this pricing technique has acquired the picturesque name of "phantom freight."

[1] The actual practice of "uniform delivered zone prices" is somewhat different from this but amounts to much the same thing.   See E. Margolin and W. P. McLendon, *Transportation Factors in the Marketing of Newsprint*, Transportation Series, no. 2, U.S. Department of Commerce, Washington, 1952.

[2] The term "netback" is defined as the delivered price to the customer less any transportation costs from the mill to the customer.   This amount represents the incremental revenue to the mill before deducting the incremental costs of manufacture.

To simplify calculations, we shall suppose that the four towns are equidistant from one another and that the freight rate between adjacent towns is $5 per ton for both the narrow and the wide sizes. The port price for the wide grade is $100 per ton and for the narrow grade, $120. The resulting marginal revenue schedules (incremental mill netbacks) are shown in Figures 5-2

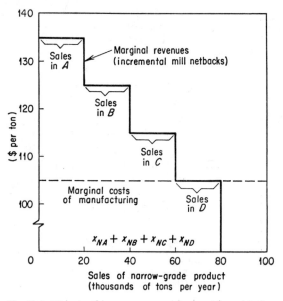

Fig. 5-3. Marginal revenues on narrow-grade product.

and 5-3. At *B*, for example, the delivered price for the wide product is

Port price at *D* + freight inland = $100 + $10 = $110 per ton

The corresponding netback to the mill located at point *A* equals the delivered price at *B* less the $5 freight from *A* to *B*. The netback to Parnassus comes to $110 − $5 = $105 per ton sold in territory *B* (Figure 5-2). Pushing the market boundary out to point *C* results in a substantial drop in the netback. Instead of $105, the mill realizes only $95 for each ton sold in that territory:

Port price at D + freight inland − freight from mill at A =
$$\$100 + \$5 - \$10 = \$95$$

This geographical example contains the essence of the econo-mist's familiar marginal revenue analysis. The greater the sales volume the enterprise attempts to capture, the lower becomes the marginal return. It is in the limiting case of perfect com-petition that marginal revenue becomes independent of the quantity sold.

Finding an optimal solution

In order to arrive at the payoff coefficients of the programming model, these revenue calculations have to be combined with estimates of marginal manufacturing cost. According to Figure 5-2, the marginal cost of manufacturing the wide-grade product remains constant at $90 per ton over the entire relevant range. Sales in territory A yield a marginal revenue of $115. When the $90 marginal cost is subtracted, the incremental payoff associ-ated with the unknown x_{WA} (wide-grade tonnage at point A) is $25 = $115 − $90. Similarly, the payoff coefficient for the unknown x_{WB} (wide-grade tonnage at B) is $15 = $105 − $90. This kind of calculation may be performed for the other six marketing variables by working with the marginal costs of $90 and $105, respectively, for manufacturing the wide-grade and narrow-grade products. The reader should check several of these coefficients and verify that the payoff function for the linear programming model can be written as follows:

$$25x_{WA} + 15x_{WB} + 5x_{WC} - 5x_{WD}$$
$$+30x_{NA} + 20x_{NB} + 10x_{NC} + 0x_{ND} \tag{5-3}$$

The simplex problem consists of maximizing the profit function (5-3), subject to the production and marketing restrictions (5-1) and (5-2), plus the usual nonnegativity constraints upon the unknowns. One characteristic of any optimal solution can be deduced immediately from the magnitude of two of the payoff coefficients in expression (5-3). No matter what the mill capacity or the market potentials happen to be, it will not pay to sell either grade of the product in market D. Why? Because the net profit coefficient of x_{WD} is negative and that of x_{ND} is zero. This means that nothing is gained by selling narrow-grade newsprint in that area and that an out-of-pocket loss of $5 will be incurred on every ton of the wide-grade product sold there. In order to justify sales to that point, either the mill will have to be able to reduce its own manufacturing or transport costs or else the f.o.b. price at D will have to increase. Under any other circumstances, the new mill will do well to avoid sales-contract commitments as far away as point D. A similar conclusion will hold true in any case that involves selling a positive-cost product at a nonpositive marginal revenue.

A specific solution to this problem can be obtained almost by direct inspection. Each variable appears in only two equations: the *common* production capacity restriction (5-1) and an *individual* upper-bound marketing constraint in (5-2). If we only knew what implicit value u to associate with the production capacity restriction (5-1), this value would immediately indicate which activities should be operated at their upper bounds, which at zero, and which at an intermediate level.

Suppose, for example, that a tentative implicit value above $25 is assigned to the plant capacity restriction (5-1). According to this tentative value, it would be unprofitable to sell even in the home market at town A. At $25, it becomes equally profitable to set activity WA at its lower limit of zero, at its upper limit of 30 thousand tons, or at any intermediate level (see Figure 5-4). And below $25 for u, it will always be profitable to set x_{WA} at its upper limit of 30 thousand tons.

Similarly, with u at $24, the payoff coefficient for activity NA just equals its opportunity cost: $30 = 1.25u$. [Note the coefficient of 1.25 for activity NA in restriction (5-1).] At $24, activity NA becomes the marginal one. Below $24, it would pay to expand this activity up to its maximum level of 20 thousand tons per year of narrow-grade, i.e., 25 thousand tons of wide-grade equivalent. An implicit price of $24 would be consistent with a plant capacity anywhere in the range between 30 and 55 thousand tons per year of wide-grade equivalent.

Each of the steps shown in Figure 5-4 corresponds to some particular activity as the marginal one and is labeled accordingly. From this figure, it is straightforward to read off the optimal

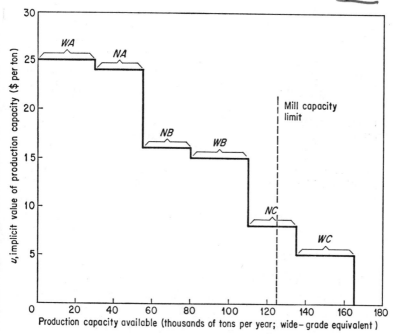

Fig. 5-4. Implicit value of production capacity.

solution corresponding to the actual capacity level of 125 thousand tons per year. This level falls within the range in which activity NC is the marginal one and the implicit worth of capacity is $8 a ton. At the $8 price, activities WA, NA, NB, and WB are at their respective upper limits, and activities WC, WD, and ND are at their lower limits of zero. The level of the marginal activity, NC, is set at 12 so that the demands for capacity just match up against the availability:

$$1.00(30 + 30) + 1.25(20 + 20 + 12) = 125$$

The optimal activity levels work out as follows:

Variables at their upper bounds:	$x_{WA} = x_{WB} = 30$
	$x_{NA} = x_{NB} = 20$
Variables at their lower bounds:	$x_{WC} = x_{WD} = 0$
	$x_{ND} = 0$
Variable at an intermediate level	$x_{NC} = 12$

In this optimal solution, only one unknown, x_{NC}, occurs at a level intermediate between its upper and its lower bound. Note also that, aside from the upper-bound restrictions on individual unknowns, there is just one restriction in this problem, the over-all capacity limitation (5-1). This pattern is no sheer coincidence. In the Appendix to this chapter, it is shown that the number of variables at intermediate levels in a basic feasible solution will never exceed the number of equations other than individual upper-bound limitations; and that this fact can be used to reduce substantially the burden of numerical computations.

Conclusions

This completes the linear programming analysis of the Parnassus newsprint problem, a perfectly straightforward one as far as it goes. Despite the fact that a downward-sloping demand curve occurred here, it was possible to translate this phenomenon into linear programming terms by defining submarkets, constant marginal revenues within each submarket, and saturation limits for each submarket. The marginal revenue obtainable from the sale of any one product was represented as a nonlinear function— one consisting of successively lower plateaus (refer back to Figures 5-2 and 5-3). The process of optimization subject to the upper-bound constraints ensures that, unless the variable x_{WA} is set at its upper bound of 30, x_{WB} will not be made positive. Similarly, unless x_{WB} is at its upper bound, x_{WC} will not be positive, and so on. No matter what sort of *descending* marginal revenue curve is involved, it will still be possible to approximate this by a staircase function within a linear programming model.[1]

If no technical problem arises in handling a downward-sloping revenue curve, where does the difficulty come up? It emerges at a very early stage in the analysis—the statistical estimation of sales potential in each of the market areas. At best, these estimates will necessarily be extremely crude ones. Whether or not price competition is ruled out, the market potential in any one area is all too likely to depend on how well a rival's sales manager gets along with an important newspaper publisher on the golf links or in the locker room.

Whenever we deal with a marketing problem, personal idiosyncrasies are bound to play a dominant role, whether the prospective customer is a gullible housewife or a supposedly hard-headed purchasing agent. Psychological motivations cannot be ignored, nor can they usually be quantified. With a linear programming model—or with any other model for that matter—we cannot expect to convert low-precision basic data into a high-precision finished model. All that can be done is to provide a framework for making decisions in a consistent manner. The only way to compensate for the necessarily low precision of any demand forecast is to make sensitivity tests with the model and to try to understand the limits within which a proposed solution will remain an optimal one—or, if not optimal, at least a fairly satisfactory one.

APPENDIX TO CHAPTER 5

Upper-bound constraints in linear programming calculations

One of the most frequent kinds of constraints to be found within a linear programming model consists of an upper bound upon the level of a single unknown. These upper bounds may

---

[1] If marginal revenues *increase* with the quantity sold, or if marginal costs decrease, the character of the problem becomes radically altered. A local optimum is no longer necessarily a global optimum, and it may be necessary to resort to integer programming. See Chaps. 6 and 7.

be imposed for a variety of reasons, but one of the most common is for the purpose of approximating a nonlinear marginal revenue or cost function as in connection with the Parnassus newsprint problem. Since these constraints show up so frequently, it is worth demonstrating that they add very little to the labor of the simplex calculation.

To fix ideas, let us return to the capital-budgeting problem discussed at the beginning of Chapter 2. There, if we denote by x_1 the number of millions of dollars to be invested at a 30 per cent annual rate of return, x_2 the number at 25 per cent, x_3 the number at 20 per cent, and x_4 the number at 15 per cent, the linear programming model can be phrased:

Maximize

$$.30x_1 + .25x_2 + .20x_3 + .15x_4 \qquad (5\text{-}4)$$

subject to the conditions:

$$
\begin{aligned}
x_1 + x_2 + x_3 + x_4 &\le 30 \\
x_1 &\le 8 \\
x_2 \phantom{{}+{}} &\le 12 \qquad (5\text{-}5)\\
x_3 \phantom{{}+{}} &\le 15 \\
x_4 &\le 10
\end{aligned}
$$

To convert the five inequalities into equalities, five slack variables are introduced: x_{10}, x_{11}, x_{12}, x_{13}, and x_{14}; and the inequalities are rewritten as follows:

$$
\begin{aligned}
x_1 + x_2 + x_3 + x_4 + x_{10} \phantom{{}+{}} &= 30 \quad (5\text{-}6)\\
x_1 \phantom{{}+ x_2 + x_3 + x_4{}} + x_{11} \phantom{{}+{}} &= 8 \quad (5\text{-}7)\\
x_2 \phantom{{}+{}} + x_{12} \phantom{{}+{}} &= 12 \quad (5\text{-}8)\\
x_3 \phantom{{}+{}} + x_{13} \phantom{{}+{}} &= 15 \quad (5\text{-}9)\\
x_4 \phantom{{}+{}} + x_{14} &= 10 \quad (5\text{-}10)
\end{aligned}
$$

Since the model contains just five equations (including the upper-bound constraints), each basis must contain exactly five out of the nine possible activities. Note also that in order for, say, equation (5-7), to be satisfied, at least one of the two activities that appear within this equation must be in the basis. In other words, either activity 1 or activity 11 or both must be in the basis. A similar statement holds for each of the three other upper-bound-constraint equations, (5-8), (5-9), and (5-10). Evidently, with each of these equations there are just two possibilities: Either a single activity from that pair or both members of the pair are in the basis. If just a single member appears, the level of that activity can be evaluated at a glance. It will be exactly equal to the right-hand-side constant indicated for the equation. If, on the other hand, both activities associated with an upper-bound constraint appear within the basis, then that upper bound is really redundant. The remainder of the system can be solved independently of the upper-bound constraint.

To illustrate these propositions, consider the optimal basis of the capital budgeting problem, a basis consisting of activities 1, 2, 3, 13, and 14. The levels of activities 1, 2, and 14 can be read off directly from their respective upper-bound-constraint equations:

$$x_1 \quad\quad = 8 \tag{5-7a}$$
$$x_2 \quad = 12 \tag{5-8a}$$
$$x_{14} = 10 \tag{5-10a}$$

The *essential* part of the basis consists of the first equation alone:

$$x_1 + x_2 + x_3 = 30 \tag{5-6a}$$

Therefore
$$x_3 = 30 - 8 - 12 = 10$$

Equation (5-9) is redundant. Now that the level of x_3 is known, this equation serves only to permit evaluation of the slack variable x_{13}:

$$x_3 + x_{13} = 15 \tag{5-9a}$$

Therefore
$$x_{13} = 15 - 10 = 5$$

This completes the process of solving for the five unknowns. To summarize: First we distinguish between the upper-bound constraints on individual unknowns and all other constraints within the linear programming model. These last are termed the essential constraints. [In the capital budgeting example, four out of the five equations comprised upper bounds and there was only one essential constraint, equation (5-6).]

Next, in the case of the upper-bound constraints for which just one of the two activities appears in the basis, we solve directly for activity levels. (This step enabled us to read off the values of x_1, x_2, and x_{14}.) We know that the remaining upper-bound constraints are redundant and serve only to evaluate the slack variables associated with those constraints. The essential equations within the basis can be solved by themselves without regard to the redundant upper-bound equations, but taking account of the activity levels already generated by the nonredundant upper bounds. Here the essential basis consisted of just one equation, and so we solved for x_3, already knowing the values of x_1, x_2, and x_{14} and not caring what value x_{13} took on—just as long as it remained nonnegative.

Last, we used equation (5-9), which may be regarded as the definition of x_{13}, an unknown that did not enter into any of the preceding equations. In this way, the complexity of the model was reduced from a five-equation system to one involving no more equations than appeared in the essential set of constraints.

Here the essential set consisted of just one equation, but even in more complicated cases, we shall continue to find that the complexity of the simultaneous system to be solved is related to the number of equations in the essential set regardless of the number of unknowns with individual upper bounds. The whole trick consists in observing that either one activity from an upper-bound equation must appear in the basis or both must appear. In the one case, the right-hand-side constant determines the activity level directly. In the other, the upper-bound equation is redundant and may be regarded as the definition of a slack variable that enters no other equation in the system. In neither case can the upper-bound constraint add substantially to the difficulties of obtaining numerical solutions.

In order to make sure that the reader has followed the argument used here, he ought to construct for himself the corresponding statement about the evaluation of implicit prices (the dual variables) in this same problem.[1]

EXERCISES

5-1. How high above $100 per ton would it be necessary for the f.o.b. price on wide rolls to rise at point D before it became desirable for the newsprint mill to increase its output of this item and cut down on the production of narrow rolls?

5-2. What adjustments would the company want to make if it found that its sales potential for narrow rolls was 25 thousand instead of 20 thousand tons in market B?   What if this total rose to 60 thousand tons per year?

5-3. Suppose that the Federal Trade Commission succeeded in obtaining a court order to enforce uniform mill net prices.   In other words, the company is now required to establish a single f.o.b. mill price on each grade of product and to use this base for adding on transportation charges from its mill to the individual consumer.   Suppose also that the f.o.b. prices at point D remain unchanged at the levels of $100 and $120 per ton and that the market potentials are also unchanged.   That is, these potentials continue to represent the amount that the mill can sell if its delivered price does not exceed the delivered price on shipments brought in from point D.

If the company wants to maximize its profits, what price should it set on its two products?   [*Hint.* The only change needed to answer this question is to alter the payoff coefficients shown in (5-3).   It helps to think of the unknowns, not as the prices to be charged, but rather as the quantities to be sold in the individual market areas.]

5-4. What effects will the new pricing practice have upon the mill's total sales volume?   Do you believe that a change to f.o.b.

[1] For further details, the reader may refer to Dantzig's original paper on the topic, "Upper Bounds, Secondary Constraints, and Block Triangularity in Linear Programming," *Econometrica*, April, 1955.

mill pricing will *necessarily* have an adverse effect upon the sales volume of the individual mill?   Upon the volume of the newsprint industry as a whole?   Which of the two kinds of pricing practice is likely to make it possible for each company within the industry to penetrate into the other's marketing territory? Which serves to increase the amount of competition within the industry?   Which promotes cross hauling of freight?[1]

[1] The reader who is interested in pursuing these matters will want to consult F. Machlup's stimulating and controversial volume, *The Basing-point System*, McGraw-Hill Book Company, Inc., The Blakiston Division, New York, 1949.

CHAPTER SIX

INTEGER PROGRAMMING

A definition

One of the basic postulates used in all linear programming is that of "proportionality." Double the amount of butter, sugar, and eggs needed to bake one pound of cake, and most housewives will agree that this second bill of materials will suffice to produce two pounds of an identical product. But when it comes to applying the postulate of proportionality in reverse, there are many women who will rightly object that you cannot necessarily halve a recipe. What if the thrifty original recipe called for only one small egg? There may be no practical way to produce just half a pound of this kind of cake at half the cost.

This is perhaps the homeliest example of the "indivisibilities" or "economies of scale" problem that so often crops up in actual decision making. Three fairly typical cases will be studied in this and the following chapter: one involving planeload versus less-than-planeload transport of passengers, one involving the expansion of plant capacity, and one involving the sequencing of jobs within a shop.

The distinguishing characteristic of each of these cases is that of an either-or choice. In the airplane case, either an entire planeload must be dispatched or none at all. In the capacity-expansion case, either a sizable plant must be built or none at all.

In the job shop sequencing problem, if two distinct jobs, A and B, are to be performed on the same piece of equipment, either job A must precede B, or the reverse must be true.

Integer programming, then, is concerned with the numerical solution of problems in which either-or choices are significant. More formally, it can be defined as the maximization of a linear form, subject to linear equality constraints, and subject also to the condition that the unknowns be nonnegative integers. In compact notation, these conditions can be written:

$$\text{Maximize} \qquad \sum_{j=1}^{n} p_j x_j \qquad\qquad (6\text{-}1)$$

subject to the conditions:

$$\sum_{j=1}^{n} a_{ij} x_j = q_i \qquad\qquad (6\text{-}2)$$

$$\text{and} \qquad x_j = 0 \text{ or } 1 \text{ or } 2 \text{ or } \ldots \qquad\qquad (6\text{-}3)$$

This all coincides with the definition of linear programming given at the beginning of Chapter 3, except the either-or constraint (6-3), the condition prescribing that the unknowns x_j be nonnegative integers. In the ordinary linear programming problem, there is no guarantee that the unknowns will take on integer values. However, we have already come across one important case in which such a guarantee exists. Every basic feasible solution to a transportation model will automatically satisfy the integer constraints provided that the column-sum availabilities and the row-sum requirements are also stated in integers. In this chapter, we shall study a technique for producing integer solutions to the more general class of problems described by conditions (6-1) to (6-3).

An air transport problem

The indivisibility of vehicles seems to be a recurrent difficulty in the analysis of almost all modes of transportation—autos, trucks, buses, railroad cars, airplanes, and ships. Given the apparent ton-mile efficiencies of large vehicles, the primary justification for the use of small units must be the indivisibilities problem, the likelihood that with such units, one will be able to achieve a higher load factor over the typical transport route.   It is also because of these indivisibilities that the typical transport network consists of trunk lines and feeder lines.   Feeder lines help make it possible to use large, efficient vehicles along the trunk lines.

The following small-scale artificial example should serve to illustrate the nature of the problem.[1]   An airline estimates that the demand for services between two points consists of 130 passengers daily.   Two types of airplane are available: a 50-passenger unit and an 80-passenger unit.   Each trip on the large airplane will cost the airline $2,400, and each trip on the small one $1,700.   (The per-seat cost is therefore $34 for the small plane and $30 for the large one.)   By simple enumeration, it is easy enough to figure out the minimum-cost solution to this problem.   The airline should use one large plane and one small plane to meet this requirement.

But suppose that this problem involved too many possible combinations for enumeration to be at all feasible.   Is there any way to proceed analytically?   Suppose that the unknown x_1 is defined as the number of daily flights in the large airplane, and x_2 the number of daily flights in the small airplane.   The minimum daily requirement for 130 seats can then be written algebraically as follows:

$$80x_1 + 50x_2 \geq 130$$
or
$$8x_1 + 5x_2 \geq 13 \qquad (6\text{-}4)$$

If, provisionally, we agree to neglect the constraint that the solution involve an integer number of airplane trips, this means that the entire shaded area in Figure 6-1 is feasible.   Our object is to select values for x_1 and x_2 so as to minimize costs and yet remain within this shaded area.   The cost expression to be

[1] Adapted from a similar problem posed by M. Beckmann and J. Laderman in "A Bound on the Use of Inefficient Indivisible Units," *Naval Research Logistics Quarterly*, December, 1956.

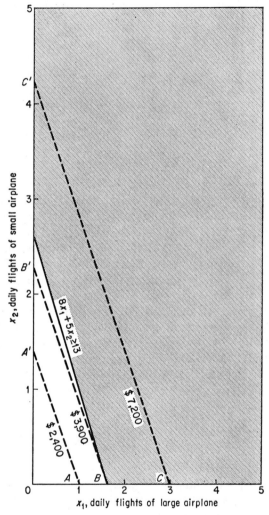

Fig. 6-1. Alternative flight possibilities.

minimized is as follows:

$$\text{Daily costs} = \$2,400x_1 + \$1,700x_2 \qquad (6\text{-}5)$$

Three members of this family of iso-cost contours are plotted as dashed lines in Figure 6-1. For example, line CC' is the locus of all combinations of x_1 and x_2 costing \$7,200 daily. Similarly, along AA' all combinations cost \$2,400. The minimum attainable cost is reached at point B along the contour line BB' corresponding to total daily expenses of \$3,900. In physical terms, point B requires no flights of the small airplane and $1\frac{3}{8}$ daily flights of the large one—an odd kind of provisional solution neglecting the integer constraints!

Fortunately, in this instance it is not too difficult to salvage things. Since the provisional solution indicates that it will take $1\frac{3}{8}$ flights of the *large* airplane in order to satisfy condition (6-4), in an integer solution there must be a combined total of at least two daily flights. Algebraically,

$$x_1 + x_2 \geq 2 \qquad (6\text{-}6)$$

If we adjoin condition (6-6) to (6-4), the resulting shaded area of feasibility is reduced to the one shown in Figure 6-2. With this added constraint, point B is no longer feasible, and the minimum-cost point shifts to D. At point D, there is one flight of each airplane type, and the total daily cost becomes \$4,100.[1] This solution in integers is qualitatively very different from the provisional one shown in Figure 6-1, in which the integer constraint was neglected. As long as one ignores the integer constraint, it never pays to utilize the smaller vehicle with its high costs per seat. But as soon as indivisibilities are taken into account, one is forced to recognize an important virtue in this kind of airplane: the fact that it is ordinarily possible to achieve higher load factors with such units.

---

[1] The minimum cost of an integer solution must always be at least as high as that of the corresponding linear program when the integer constraints are neglected.

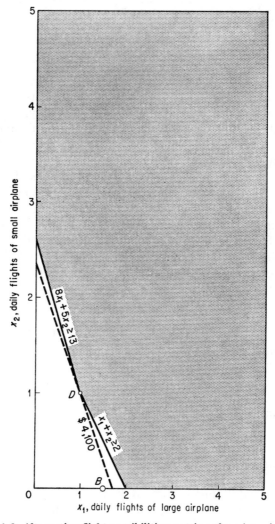

Fig. 6-2. Alternative flight possibilities: cutting plane introduced.

A general technique for integer programming

The procedure just described represents more than just an improvisation designed to exploit the numerical features of this particular example. It yields a clue toward understanding the general method devised by Gomory for solving integer programming problems.[1] In essence, his approach consists in obtaining a provisional linear programming solution by first ignoring the integer constraints. Then if any unknowns fail to take on integer values, Gomory's method will automatically generate a "cutting plane" similar to condition (6-6). Such a cutting plane excludes the current fractional solution but remains a legitimate condition that will necessarily have to be satisfied by *any* solution in integers. After this cutting plane has been adjoined to the original linear equality constraints (6-2), one solves for a new optimal solution ignoring the integer constraints (6-3). If this new solution is in integers, one may stop. Otherwise, one again produces a cutting plane, adjoins this to the previously enlarged problem, and optimizes once more. This general procedure will produce an optimal solution in a finite number of steps.

In order to understand Gomory's automatic technique for generating cutting planes, we must first take a slight mathematical detour to define the concepts of "congruence" and of "fractional part." We shall say that the number a is congruent to b if, and only if, their difference, $a - b$, is an integer. Algebraically,

$$a \equiv b \qquad \text{if, and only if, } a - b \text{ is an integer}$$

For example, $\tfrac{7}{4} \equiv \tfrac{3}{4}$
Also $-\tfrac{1}{4} \equiv \tfrac{3}{4}$

The fractional part of a number a is written $f(a)$ and is defined as the smallest nonnegative number congruent to a.

[1] R. E. Gomory, "Outline of an Algorithm for Integer Solutions to Linear Programs," *Bulletin of the American Mathematical Society*, September, 1958. Also by Gomory, "An Algorithm for Integer Solutions to Linear Programs," Princeton-IBM Mathematics Research Project Technical Report, no. 1, Sept. 17, 1958.

For example, $\quad f(\frac{7}{4}) = f(-\frac{1}{4}) = \frac{3}{4}$
For example, $\quad f(3) = f(2) = f(1) = 0$

Now let us apply these ideas to the air-transport problem. The original conditions may be written as follows:

Mimimize $\qquad\qquad \$2,400x_1 + \$1,700x_2 \qquad\qquad$ (6-5)

subject to the conditions:

$$8x_1 + 5x_2 - x_3 = 13 \qquad\qquad (6\text{-}7)$$
and $\qquad\qquad x_1, x_2, x_3 = 0, 1, 2, 3, \ldots$

where x_3 is a newly defined slack variable. Since x_1, x_2, and the passenger load capabilities are all integers, the slack variable x_3 must also take on integer values.

In the provisional optimal solution neglecting the integer constraints, (6-7) may be rewritten as follows, transferring the nonbasic variables x_2 and x_3 to the right-hand side,

$$x_1 = 1\tfrac{3}{8} - \tfrac{5}{8}x_2 + \tfrac{1}{8}x_3 \qquad\qquad (6\text{-}8)$$

Denote an *integer* solution to this problem by the primed variables x_1', x_2', and x_3'. These primed values also satisfy (6-8); therefore $\qquad x_1' = 1\tfrac{3}{8} - \tfrac{5}{8}x_2' + \tfrac{1}{8}x_3' \qquad\qquad (6\text{-}9)$

Since the left-hand side (L.H.S.) of (6-9) is an integer, the right-hand side (R.H.S.) must be congruent to zero:

$$1\tfrac{3}{8} - \tfrac{5}{8}x_2' + \tfrac{1}{8}x_3' \equiv 0$$
therefore $\qquad\qquad \tfrac{5}{8}x_2' - \tfrac{1}{8}x_3' \equiv 1\tfrac{3}{8} \qquad\qquad (6\text{-}10)$

Taking fractional parts on both sides and recalling that x_2' and x_3' are both integers,[1]

---

[1] The manipulations by which we obtain (6-10) and (6-11) are based upon the following properties of the congruence relation and the fractional part operation:

1. If $a \equiv b$, then $-a \equiv -b$
2. If $a \equiv b$, then for all c, $a + c \equiv b + c$
3. If $a \equiv b$, then $f(a) = f(b)$
4. $f(a + b) \equiv f(a) + f(b)$
5. If n is an integer, then for all a,

$$na \equiv f(na) \equiv nf(a)$$

$$f(\tfrac{5}{8})x_2' + f(-\tfrac{1}{8})x_3' \equiv f(1\tfrac{3}{8})$$

therefore
$$\tfrac{5}{8}x_2' + \tfrac{7}{8}x_3' \equiv \tfrac{5}{8} \qquad (6\text{-}11)$$

Since all fractional parts are defined so as to be nonnegative, the L.H.S. of (6-11) must be nonnegative. Nonnegativity and *also* congruence to $\tfrac{5}{8}$ imply

$$\tfrac{5}{8}x_2' + \tfrac{7}{8}x_3' = \tfrac{5}{8} \text{ or } 1\tfrac{3}{8} \text{ or } 2\tfrac{1}{8} \text{ or } \ldots$$

or
$$\tfrac{5}{8}x_2' + \tfrac{7}{8}x_3' \geq \tfrac{5}{8} \qquad (6\text{-}12)$$

At last, a cutting plane has been produced. Condition (6-12) is *not* satisfied by the provisional fractional solution (6-8); yet by our congruence argument we have shown that any solution in integers must satisfy (6-12). For convenience, this inequality may be written in the form of an equality, introducing x_4 as a nonnegative integer-valued slack variable:[1]

$$\tfrac{5}{8}x_2' + \tfrac{7}{8}x_3' - x_4 = \tfrac{5}{8} \qquad (6\text{-}13)$$

Adjoining (6-13) to (6-7), we again optimize in the ordinary linear programming way, provisionally neglecting the integer constraints. This time we find that our optimal basis consists of activities 1 and 2 and that $x_1 = x_2 = 1$. With this result, our job is completed.

Through a process of direct elimination, equations (6-7) and (6-13) may also be written in "diagonal" form so that each of the basic variables x_1 and x_2 is expressed as a constant term plus a linear function of the nonbasic variables x_3 and x_4:

$$\begin{aligned} x_1 &= 1 + 1x_3 - 1x_4 \\ x_2 &= 1 - \tfrac{7}{5}x_3 + \tfrac{8}{5}x_4 \end{aligned} \qquad (6\text{-}14)$$

If in this new provisional solution either x_1 or x_2 had turned out at fractional values, we would again be in a position to apply the line of reasoning that began with (6-8), to generate a cutting plane such as (6-12), and to use this plane to find a new provisional solution. This process can be repeated indefinitely until an optimum integer solution has been produced.

---

[1] In order to preserve the congruence relationship specified by (6-11), the slack variable x_4 must itself be an integer.

Several technical remarks: (1) This line of reasoning all depends upon diagonalizing the original equations into the form of (6-14), with each of the basis variables expressed as independent of the other basis variables. (2) If, in a provisional noninteger solution written in diagonal form, two or more of the basis activities appear at noninteger levels, the best row from which to construct the new cutting plane is apparently that one for which the R.H.S. constant term has the largest fractional part. (3) The coefficients of $+1$ and $-\frac{7}{5}$ associated with activity 3 on the R.H.S. of (6-14) are identical with what we have previously labeled Δ_1 and Δ_2, the unit adjustments in the basis variables per unit of activity 3 introduced into the basis. And similarly, this is true of the coefficients of activity 4; respectively, -1 and $+\frac{8}{5}$.

A summary of the cutting plane technique

In any particular basic feasible solution, let the basic variables be denoted by x_j and the nonbasic ones by x_k. In diagonal form, we then have:

$$x_j = \hat{q}_j + \sum_k \hat{a}_{jk} x_k \qquad j = 1 \cdots m \qquad (6\text{-}15)$$

where the constants $\hat{q}_j$ and the coefficients $\hat{a}_{jk}$ represent transformed values of the original constants q_i and the original coefficients a_{ij}.

The cutting plane is constructed from the ith row, the one for which the fractional part, $f(\hat{q}_j)$, is largest. Letting x_i' and x_k' denote, respectively, integer values of the ith row's basic variable and the kth nonbasic variable,

$$x_i' = \hat{q}_i + \sum_k \hat{a}_{ik} x_k' \qquad (6\text{-}16)$$

therefore $\qquad 0 \equiv \hat{q}_i + \sum_k \hat{a}_{ik} x_k'$

therefore $\qquad \sum_k (-\hat{a}_{ik}) x_k' \equiv \hat{q}_i$

therefore $\qquad \sum_k [f(-\hat{a}_{ik})] x_k' \equiv f(\hat{q}_i)$

This finally produces the cutting plane

$$\sum_k [f(-\hat{a}_{ik})]x'_k \geq f(\hat{q}_i) \tag{6-17}$$

In the airplane problem, for example,

$$x_1 = 1\tfrac{3}{8} - \tfrac{5}{8}x_2 + \tfrac{1}{8}x_3 \tag{6-8}$$

The cutting plane was produced as follows:

$$[f(\tfrac{5}{8})]x'_2 + [f(-\tfrac{1}{8})]x'_3 \geq f(1\tfrac{3}{8})$$
$$\tfrac{5}{8}x'_2 + \tfrac{7}{8}x'_3 \geq \tfrac{5}{8} \tag{6-12}$$

Capacity expansion

The Titanic Chemical Corporation is considering the possibility of setting up a West Coast manufacturing operation in order to satisfy the growing market for one of its products there. Because of the lead time required for new construction, the earliest possible date for such a new plant would be in two years. The Western demand for this product is estimated at 2 million pounds per year during the first two years after the possible establishment of a plant and is projected at the stable rate of 5 million pounds per year indefinitely thereafter.

One alternative would be to continue to meet this demand by bringing in the product from existing facilities on the East Coast. These supplementary shipments, however, are expensive. For each pound brought in from the East Coast, the company will incur marginal costs of $.30 in excess of those that would be involved in a West Coast manufacturing operation. (This $.30 per pound differential takes account only of current costs and does not involve any interest or depreciation on the original investment.)

The other alternative, West Coast manufacturing operations, entails the problem of economies of scale in the construction of the new plant. Each time that a new plant for this product is set up, Titanic has found that a minimum investment cost of $.75 million is incurred, regardless of the amount of capacity

104   Economic Analysis for Business Decisions

installed.   In addition to this setup cost, a variable investment
cost of $1 per pound of annual capacity must also be met.   The
total investment figures corresponding to the three relevant
plant-size possibilities are therefore:

Capacity, millions of pounds a year	Initial investment cost, millions of dollars	Investment cost per pound of annual capacity
2	$2.75	$1.375
3	3.75	1.250
5	5.75	1.150

In order to complete the statement of this problem, one more
factor must be introduced: the time worth of money.   It will
be assumed that the Titanic Chemical Corporation has alternative investment opportunities yielding 20 per cent per annum
into the indefinite future.   Hence the present worth of $1 of
costs incurred at time t equals $.8^t$.   Like most investment problems, this is one in which the time worth of money plays a crucial
role.   This consideration places a significant penalty upon the
decision to proceed immediately with the establishment of a
low-cost 5-million-pound plant.

From these data, a programming problem may be constructed
involving six integer-valued unknowns:

x_1 = amount of capacity installed at the beginning of the first
two-year time phase (millions of pounds per year)

x_2 = amount of capacity installed after the end of the first two-
year time phase (millions of pounds per year)

x_3 = fraction of $.75 million setup charge incurred at the begin-
ning of the first two-year phase (x_3 = 0 or 1)

x_4 = fraction of $.75 million setup charge incurred after the end
of the first two-year phase (x_4 = 0 or 1)

x_5 = annual rate of supplementary shipments during the first
two-year phase

x_6 = annual rate of supplementary shipments maintained after
the end of the first two-year phase

The first group of constraints spells out the fairly obvious restriction that, during each of the two phases, the amount of newly installed plus inherited capacity plus supplementary shipments must be at least as great as the West Coast demand:

$$x_1 + x_5 \geq 2$$
$$x_1 + x_2 + x_6 \geq 5 \tag{6-18}$$

The second group of conditions is related to the fixed-charge activities at unknown fractional levels x_3 and x_4. These conditions are designed expressly to take advantage of the either-or nature of integer programming. They ensure that either a fixed charge of $.75 million is incurred or else no capacity is installed. The first condition, for example, relates to the beginning of the first phase. It specifies that, if any positive amount of capacity is installed at that time, i.e., if $x_1 > 0$, the fraction x_3 must be set at a positive level, therefore unity, and that 100 per cent of the fixed investment cost must be spent. (This inequality implies that the unknown x_3 can be zero only if x_1 is also zero.) The second inequality expresses a similar relationship between x_2 and x_4, the amounts of capacity, and the fraction of the fixed charge incurred at the beginning of the second phase. These particular inequalities depend upon our initial knowledge that the amount of capacity installed will in no case exceed 5 million pounds:

$$5x_3 \geq x_1$$
$$5x_4 \geq x_2 \tag{6-19}$$

Subject to conditions (6-18) and (6-19), the programming problem consists of selecting nonnegative integer values for $x_1, x_2, \ldots, x_6$ in such a way as to minimize the present value of all cash expenditures:[1]

---

[1] Since all outlays are treated on a discounted cash-flow basis, depreciation expenses may be disregarded. Interest costs and obsolescence probabilities are taken into account by the present-worth factor.

Present value of cash expenditures (millions of dollars) $=$

$$\begin{aligned} &1.00[.8^2x_1 + .8^4x_2] \\ &+.75[.8^2x_3 + .8^4x_4] \\ &+.30\left[(.8^{2.5} + .8^{3.5})x_5 + (.8^{4.5})\left(\frac{1}{1-.8}\right)x_6\right] \end{aligned}$$

(6-20)

In the minimand (6-20), all the present-value factors are based upon an initial construction lag of two years for the new plant. Present values for plant construction costs are therefore reckoned as of the two dates of possible completion: two and four years hence. But since any supplementary shipment costs would be incurred continuously in time, the present values of such shipments are reckoned as of the midpoint of each future year. In the coefficient associated with the unknown x_6, the term $1/(1 - .8)$ reflects the fact that, during the phase of stationary demand, any supplementary shipments would have to be sustained into the indefinite future.

EXERCISES

6-1. Solve the Titanic Chemical problem by direct enumeration rather than through integer programming, and determine the optimal pattern of expansion. Would your conclusions be significantly affected if it turned out that the West Coast plant became obsolete in 15 years instead of in the indefinite future?

6-2. Calculate a new solution to the air transport problem discussed earlier in this chapter, based upon a cost increase for the small airplane from $1,700 to $2,000 per trip. Use Gomory's method for the automatic generation of cutting planes. Be sure to calculate implicit prices and to verify the optimality of each intermediate linear programming solution.

6-3. Mercury Airlines has a fixed policy of utilizing no more than one airplane type along a given route. Cost and capacity data for the two alternative types available are as follows:

	Type number 505	Type number 507
Cost per trip..............	$4,000	$6,300
Passenger capacity........	40	70

Draw a chart indicating the ranges of daily passenger volumes within which each of these units is advantageous.

CHAPTER SEVEN

SEQUENCING PROBLEMS

The Gantt chart

Still another example of integer programming occurs in connection with job sequencing for batch-type production processes. The characteristic feature of these batch processes is that a given piece of equipment cannot be employed simultaneously for handling more than one item. This either-or feature differs quite sharply from most of the continuous-process cases examined thus far, e.g., oil refining, in which the problem of sequencing is of secondary importance.

Traditionally, in order to analyze batch-type scheduling, the industrial engineer has used a device known as a Gantt chart. After reviewing the nature of such charts, we shall then demonstrate how batching problems can be approached by integer programming. In order to keep things as simple as possible, we shall suppose that there are only two jobs to be processed, the printing and the binding of books A and B, and that the objective of the scheduler is to minimize the make-span, the total time elapsing before both books are ready to be shipped out.[1] The only bottleneck stage of the process is the first one, printing. There is enough binding equipment available so that both jobs

---

[1] This example is adapted from one employed by S. Johnson in his important paper, "Optimal Two and Three Stage Production Schedules and Setup Times Included," *Naval Research Logistics Quarterly*, March, 1954.

could proceed simultaneously at this stage. Printing and binding times for the two items are:

Stage	Book A	Book B
Printing time.........	1 week	2 weeks
Binding time.........	1 week	3 weeks

Two Gantt charts have been constructed from these data, each in accordance with a different rule of thumb. Figure 7-1 is based upon the rule of "shortest impending process time." According to this, the scheduler should award priority to job A, since its printing time is less than that of B. Figure 7-2 is based upon another popular rule: "maximum remaining process time." According to this second rule, priority should be given to book B, since the total of its printing plus binding times comes to 5 weeks in comparison with only 2 weeks for book A.

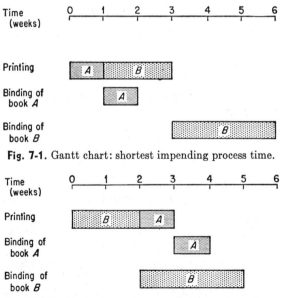

Fig. 7-1. Gantt chart: shortest impending process time.

Fig. 7-2. Gantt chart: maximum remaining process time.

Here it is simple enough to construct all possible Gantt charts, to examine all alternative priority rules, and to arrive at the obvious result. If the objective is taken to be one of minimizing the make-span, the job dispatcher should follow the plan of Figure 7-2, giving priority to book B, thereby completing both books in only 5 weeks, in comparison with the 6 weeks required for the Gantt chart of Figure 7-1.

This artificial example is all too easy. In actual production processes, it frequently happens that there are a dozen or more possible bottleneck points and hundreds of jobs to be scheduled. The number of alternative Gantt charts then mounts astronomically, and simple enumeration is out of the question. Under these circumstances, one very promising approach consists of computer simulation, letting a computer construct Gantt charts either purely at random or by following a variety of plausible rules, such as shortest impending process time. A number of studies have been conducted along these lines and have demonstrated the feasibility of analyzing large-scale realistic shops.[1] Another approach—still in the experimental stage—is that of integer programming, which is described below.

An integer programming formulation

In the book printing and binding problem, six integer-valued unknowns are employed:

x_1 = start date for printing book A
x_2 = start date for printing book B
x_3 = start date for binding book A
x_4 = start date for binding book B
x_5 = make-span, i.e., completion date for printing and binding both books
x_6 = fraction of book A printed before the printing of book B is begun

[1] Two reports on simulation are particularly worthwhile: J. Heller, "Some Numerical Experiments for an $M \times J$ Flow Shop," *Operations Research*, March–April, 1960; and C. J. Baker and B. P. Dzielinski, "Simulation of a Simplified Job Shop," *Management Science*, April, 1960.

Figure 7-2 enables us to read off the optimum values of these unknowns immediately:

$$x_1 = 2 \text{ weeks} \quad x_3 = 3 \text{ weeks} \quad x_5 = 5 \text{ weeks}$$
$$x_2 = 0 \text{ weeks} \quad x_4 = 2 \text{ weeks} \quad x_6 = 0 \text{ weeks}$$

Disregarding this advance knowledge, let us proceed with the business of formulation as an integer programming problem. The thing to be minimized is supposedly the make-span x_5. We must, however, observe both the sequencing restraints for each job and the noninterference condition at the printing bottleneck. First, the sequencing restraints specify that the binding of each book cannot be begun until the corresponding printing job has been completed:

$$\begin{aligned} x_3 &\geq x_1 + 1 \\ x_4 &\geq x_2 + 2 \end{aligned} \tag{7-1}$$

Second, the sequencing restraints specify that the make-span must be at least as great as the start date of binding plus the binding time for each job:

$$x_5 \geq x_3 + 1 \tag{7-2}$$
$$x_5 \geq x_4 + 3 \tag{7-2a}$$

Next come the noninterference restraints. These are the ones that hinge critically upon the either-or nature of integer programming. They ensure either that 100 per cent of the printing of book A is completed before the beginning of B or that, alternatively, 100 per cent of the printing of B is completed before the beginning of A. As an either-or condition, not yet in integer programming form, we would have:

either $\qquad\qquad x_1 - x_2 \geq 2$
or $\qquad\qquad\quad x_2 - x_1 \geq 1$ $\qquad$ (7-3)

In order to convert (7-3) into integer programming form, we take advantage of one bit of initial information that is always available in problems of this sort. The maximum difference between the start dates of the two printing jobs cannot possibly exceed the total time required to perform all operations:

$$1 + 1 + 2 + 3 = 7 \text{ weeks}$$

(See if you can find an even lower bound to this possible difference.)   In any event, therefore,

$$-7 \leq x_1 - x_2 \leq +7$$

Now we can write two *simultaneous* conditions upon the
integer-valued unknowns.   Together, these rule out any possibility of conflicts in printing dates:

$$(x_1 - x_2) + x_6(7 + 2) \geq 2 \qquad (7\text{-}4)$$
$$(x_2 - x_1) + (1 - x_6)(7 + 1) \geq 1 \qquad (7\text{-}5)$$

The effect of these conditions upon the integer-valued-unknown
fraction x_6 can be summarized as follows:

$$\text{If } (x_1 - x_2) \begin{cases} > 0 \\ = 0 \\ < 0 \end{cases}, \text{ then by (7-4), } x_6 = \begin{cases} 0 \text{ or } 1 \text{ or } 2 \text{ or } \ldots \\ 1 \text{ or } 2 \text{ or } \ldots \\ 1 \text{ or } 2 \text{ or } \ldots \end{cases}$$

$$\text{and by (7-5), } x_6 = \begin{cases} 0 \\ 0 \\ 0 \text{ or } 1 \end{cases}$$

Note that, if $x_1 = x_2$, there is no integer value for x_6 that will
simultaneously satisfy both (7-4) and (7-5).   If, on the other
hand, $x_1 \neq x_2$, x_6 will be set at a value of either zero or unity
depending upon which job is to precede the other.   Conditions
(7-4) and (7-5) then ensure that the one job will be initiated in
sufficient time to be completed before the beginning of the other
one.   For example, with $x_6 = 0$, job B is to be printed before A
(or $x_1 > x_2$).   According to (7-4), this requires that at least two
weeks be allowed between the two start dates in order to complete the printing of B.

So much for the statement of the job scheduling problem in
integer programming form: Minimize the make-span x_5 subject
to the sequencing and the noninterference restrictions (7-1), (7-2),

(7-2a), (7-4), and (7-5).   Here is one more instance of the development of integer programming opening a way to attack long-standing problems that defied formulation in terms of the conventional linear programming model.

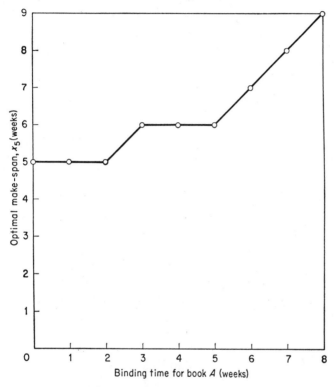

Fig. 7-3. Effect of binding time upon make-span.

By now, the reader must be well aware that there are very few problems in economic analysis in which one is concerned with a single numerical optimization.   Much more typically, an optimal solution is intended only as a jumping-off point for further calculations: testing the solution for its sensitivity with respect to the payoff coefficients, the constant terms, and the input-output coefficients. In the case of linear programming, sensitivity testing is greatly facilitated by the fact that small changes in the parameters lead to only small changes in the total payoff. As long as the basis remains unchanged, each of the constant terms can be altered without affecting the increment in payoff per unit change in that term. The entire notion of implicit prices is based upon this fact.

Integer programming, by contrast, is a much more razor's-edge affair. In any such problem, small changes in a constant term are likely to lead to discontinuous changes in the optimal payoff and to "nonconvexity." In restriction (7-2), consider the effect of varying the constant term, the binding time required for book A (see Figure 7-3). Within the range of 0 to 2 weeks, there is literally no effect of binding time upon make-span. Within the range of 3 to 5 weeks for binding, the make-span remains at a new plateau of 6 weeks, and so on. With this pattern of irregular behavior, it is apparent that the implicit prices of an integer programming calculation are virtually useless for purposes of sensitivity testing. For integer programming models, we are no longer entitled to claim that these prices measure the effect of small changes in the constant terms. With integer programming, the discouraging feature is that almost any sensitivity test—no matter how minor the departure from the initial problem—requires a complete recalculation of the optimal solution.

EXERCISES

7-1. By direct inspection, read off an optimal solution to the book scheduling problem, *neglecting* the integer constraints upon all unknowns.

7-2. What do you think of the plausibility of such rules of thumb as shortest impending process time and maximum remaining process time? How would their relative merits be affected by randomness in actual processing time?

7-3. Suppose that the shop has promised the delivery of book A at week 1 and of B at week 3. Each week of delay involves contractual penalty costs of $100 and $200, respectively. Read off the corresponding total penalties in Figures 7-1 and 7-2. Formulate the problem of minimizing these penalty costs by integer programming.

7-4. Suppose that the shop owned just one unit of equipment for binding as well as just one for printing. Construct the possible Gantt charts for this case. How would you modify the original integer programming problem in such a way as to guarantee noninterference at the binding step?

CHAPTER EIGHT

INVENTORY CONTROL

Probabilities versus point estimates

One characteristic has been common to all the cases analyzed up to this point: the absence of random elements and of uncertainties. Each analysis has proceeded as though a firm could correct for the presence of randomness in, say, a seasonal inventory storage problem, by simply inserting a point estimate, e.g., the mean plus two standard deviations, in place of a probability distribution of demand. True, such a deterministic analysis will frequently yield valuable clues toward a sensible pattern of behavior for the more relevant case: that of randomness in demand. But not always! In the three remaining chapters, we shall be concerned with an important class of problems in which the point estimate approach is particularly likely to be misleading: the area of inventory control.[1] These three chapters

---

[1] In the interest of brevity, this volume omits two other major topics in which randomness plays a dominant role: queuing theory and portfolio selection. On this latter, see H. Markowitz, *Portfolio Selection: Efficient Diversification of Investments*, John Wiley & Sons, Inc., New York, 1959. A readable introduction to the literature in queuing theory, simulation, and Monte Carlo methods may be found in M. Sasieni, A. Yaspan, and L. Friedman, *Operations Research: Methods and Problems*, John Wiley & Sons, Inc., New York, 1959, chap. 6.

presuppose that the reader has previously been introduced to the fundamentals of probability theory and that he is familiar with the definitions of a probability density function and of a cumulative distribution. In addition, some knowledge of calculus is required here.

Our first example will involve just a single replenishment decision. Later examples will involve sequential decision problems: cases in which the initial move must take account of the fact that additional information on demand will be available at the time of making subsequent decisions. The first example represents a modified version of the Apollo Antifreeze case that appeared at the end of Chapter 4. Here, instead of supposing that demand during the peak season is known in advance to be $490 + 360 = 850$ thousand gallons, the peak demand will be regarded as a random variable which is equally likely to fall anywhere within the interval between 700 thousand and 1 million gallons and which therefore has a mean of 850 thousand. In the language of probability theory, we shall refer to this demand as a continuous random variable z, to its density function as $p(z)$, and to its descending cumulative distribution as

$$P(z \geq x) = \int_{z=x}^{\infty} p(z)\, dz$$

(See Figures 8-1a and b.) The density function $p(z)$ in Figure 8-1a measures the probability with which demand lies between z and $z + dz$ units. The descending cumulative distribution function appears in Figure 8-1b and measures the probability with which the demand z will be equal to or greater than the level x. The mean demand $\bar{z}$ is defined in the usual way:

$$\bar{z} = \int_{z=0}^{\infty} zp(z)\, dz = \int_{700}^{1,000} z(\tfrac{1}{300})\, dz = 850$$

In order to focus upon the key element here—randomness in demand during the peak season—we shall simplify a number of the details previously considered. First, the analysis will proceed as though there were only two seasons of the year: the peak (fall and winter) and the off-peak (spring and summer). Sec-

ond, it will be supposed that the decision on over-all availability
of peak-season supplies x (inventories carried forward plus
contractual commitments for outside purchases plus peak-season

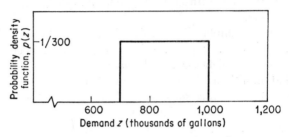

Fig. 8-1a. Density function of demand.

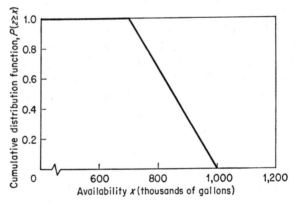

Fig. 8-1b. Cumulative distribution of demand.

production) must be made before learning the actual peak-
season demand.   The marginal cost of increasing these peak-
season supplies will be presumed constant at $2 per gallon, the
cost of outside purchases.

The company faces a twofold dilemma: If demand exceeds the
available supplies, there will be a considerable loss in potential
profits.   With a selling price of $3 and marginal costs of $2,
the company will be out of pocket by $1 for each gallon of lost
sales, to say nothing of additional losses in customer good will

and in repeat sales. If, on the other hand, the supplies exceed demand, Apollo will incur extra costs of storage from the peak into the off-peak season, say, $.50 per gallon of carryover. The inventory optimization consists in selecting an availability level x so as to minimize the total *expected* costs of storage and of lost sales.

Figure 8-2 contains a plot of the expected incremental benefits from reduction in lost sales versus the availability level x, and

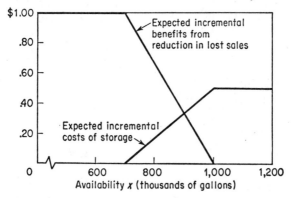

Fig. 8-2. Expected costs and benefits from alternative availability levels.

also a plot of the expected incremental storage costs versus x. Below an availability of 700 thousand, for example, an extra gallon is sure to be sold. Below 700 thousand, therefore, the expected incremental benefit from an additional gallon is the full profit margin of $1 and the expected incremental storage cost is zero. At an availability level of 850 thousand, however, there is only a 50-50 chance that an extra unit will be sold. At this level, the expected benefits from an additional gallon drop to $.50 and expected storage costs rise to $.25.

Evidently, the optimum availability level is 900 thousand— 50 thousand above the mean of 850 thousand gallons. At 900 thousand, the probability of selling an extra unit drops down to $\frac{1}{3}$. The marginal expected benefits of protection against a lost sale are only $\frac{1}{3}(\$1)$, and these benefits are just offset by the expected marginal costs of storage, $\frac{2}{3}(\$.50)$.

Now to generalize a bit: Let b denote the cost per unit of surplus inventory carried over into the off-peak season, and c the loss in profits per unit of shortage. (In the numerical example above, $b = \$.50$ and $c = \$1.$) The sum total of expected shortage plus inventory costs TEC(x) depends upon the availability level x and may be written as follows:

$$\begin{pmatrix} \text{unit} \\ \text{carryover} \\ \text{cost} \end{pmatrix}\begin{pmatrix} \text{expected} \\ \text{number} \\ \text{of units} \\ \text{carried over} \end{pmatrix} + \begin{pmatrix} \text{unit} \\ \text{shortage} \\ \text{penalty} \end{pmatrix}\begin{pmatrix} \text{expected} \\ \text{number of} \\ \text{shortages} \end{pmatrix}$$

$$b\int_{z=0}^{x}(x-z)p(z)\,dz \quad + \quad c\int_{z=x}^{\infty}(z-x)p(z)\,dz \qquad (8\text{-}1)$$

Differentiating (8-1) with respect to the decision variable x and setting the derivative equal to zero[1]

$$b\int_{z=0}^{x}p(z)\,dz + c\int_{z=x}^{\infty}-p(z)\,dz = 0$$

or
$$b\int_{z=0}^{x}p(z)\,dz = c\int_{z=x}^{\infty}p(z)\,dz \qquad (8\text{-}2)$$

[The reader should prove for himself that the second derivative of (8-1) is never negative and that condition (8-2) must always lead to a cost minimum rather than a maximum.]

Equation (8-2) provides a rigorous justification for the antifreeze inventory level of 900 thousand. In order to obtain minimum costs, the supply x should be chosen in such a way that the marginal costs of storage are just offset by the marginal

[1] It can be shown that, in order to differentiate an integral with respect to a variable that appears both in the integrand and in the limits of integration,

$$\frac{d}{dx}\left[\int_{z=g(x)}^{h(x)}f(x,z)\,dz\right] = \int_{z=g(x)}^{h(x)}\frac{\partial f(x,z)\,dz}{\partial x} + \frac{dh(x)}{dx}f[x,h(x)] - \frac{dg(x)}{dx}f[x,g(x)]$$

For example,

$$\frac{d}{dx}\left[\int_{z=0}^{x}(x-z)p(z)\,dz\right] = \int_{z=0}^{x}p(z)\,dz + 1[(x-x)p(x)]$$
$$-0[(x-0)p(0)]$$
$$= \int_{z=0}^{x}p(z)\,dz$$

benefits of reduction in lost sales, each multiplied by the respective probabilities of surplus and shortage. At $x = 900$,

$$b \int_{z=0}^{900} p(z) \, dz = c \int_{z=900}^{\infty} p(z) \, dz$$
$$(\$.50)(\tfrac{2}{3}) = (\$1)(\tfrac{1}{3})$$

Condition (8-2) may be rewritten in a form more convenient for numerical analysis—a form that indicates directly the probability of a shortage:

$$P(z \geq x) = \int_{z=x}^{\infty} p(z) \, dz = \frac{b}{b+c} \tag{8-3}$$

For example,

$$P(z \geq 900) = \int_{z=900}^{\infty} p(z) \, dz = \frac{\$.50}{\$.50 + \$1} = \frac{1}{3}$$

The higher the level of shortage penalties relative to inventory costs, the more it pays to invest in inventory in order to avert shortages. According to (8-3), stockage levels ought to be set in accordance with the relative penalties for overshooting and undershooting the demand.[1]

Estimation of shortage penalty costs

Like most academic-style instruction, this book concentrates upon problems that are deceptively easy to analyze. The much more open-ended problem of implementation is always left up to the practitioner. (There is ample precedent for such division of labor, e.g., the physicist and the engineer—or the biologist and the physician.) It is all very well to have constructed an inventory model assuming that the practitioner has somehow made an estimate of the shortage costs c. But how is he ever to go about estimating such an intangible kind of cost?

[1] Even when shortage and surplus costs are identical, i.e., when $b = c$, equation (8-3) indicates that the optimum value for x is not necessarily the mean demand, but rather the median.

How often will it be legitimate to suppose that the shortage cost on a salable item is simply the difference between marginal cost and selling price? If Apollo is in a sufficiently strong market position, it is conceivable that 60 per cent of its customers are going to be forced to wait until the company can supply them with additional quantities of antifreeze. In this case, the amount of profits forgone will amount to only $.40 per gallon of shortage rather than the initial figure of $1. If, on the other hand, the company loses all its disappointed customers and also expects to lose their patronage for the next three years, the appropriate penalty will rise to $4 per gallon of shortage.

To what extent would a fourfold increase in penalty costs affect the inventory stockage decision? According to condition (8-3), the availability level x would then have to be increased so that the probability of a shortage drops to only $\frac{1}{9} = .50/(.50 + 4)$. In order to achieve this amount of protection, the company ought to increase the supply from 900 to 967 units. Here, as in many applications, a radical change in shortage penalties leads to a comparatively minor change in the optimal stockage level. This kind of insensitivity is frequently the only saving feature that permits the construction of a usable analysis out of highly conjectural basic data.

A sequential decision model of inventory control: The EOQ case

The Apollo Antifreeze inventory model was based upon a situation in which the bulk of sales occurred during a single peak season of the year. A similar, but by no means identical, problem is concerned with the management of inventories when demands are random and when the probability distribution of demand remains constant from one season to the next. (The demand for most electronic spare parts is of this nature, but not the demand for outboard motor spares!)

In these sequential ordering problems, an additional cost element usually becomes important: the fixed cost of placing an order regardless of order size. These ordering costs may reflect not only record keeping, handling, and inspection expenses for the inventory holder but also setup costs in production, or alternatively the fact that suppliers offer quantity discounts for large shipments. The presence of this kind of cost makes it economical to order in large batches rather than to purchase one at a time as inventories become depleted.

The sequential ordering problem can best be understood by starting with a deterministic version, the economic order quantity

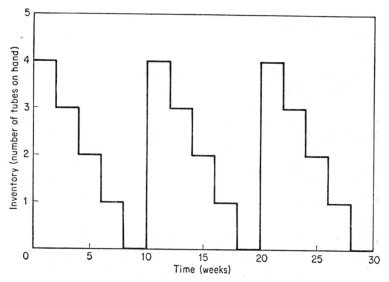

Fig. 8-3. A time series of inventory: the EOQ case.

(EOQ) model—one in which demands keep recurring at a steady annual rate of D units. Figure 8-3, for example, plots the inventory of a regional warehouse in which one unit of a certain electronic tube is demanded every other week. The annual demand rate D therefore amounts to 25 tubes per 50-week year.[1] It takes slightly less than four weeks from the time an order is placed until a replenishment shipment actually arrives at the warehouse from the manufacturing plant. Since the EOQ model assumes *perfect* timing in demands and incoming ship-

---

[1] This allows for a two-week annual vacation, partly to benefit the employees and partly to simplify our arithmetic.

ments, a replenishment order will be placed whenever the stock on hand drops to the reorder level of one unit (weeks 6, 16, and 26). Two weeks later, a new demand will deplete the inventory to a zero level. And in two more weeks, the replenishment order will come through, just in the nick of time, a few minutes ahead of the incoming order on weeks 10, 20, and 30. In such a conveniently deterministic world, there is no need to incur lost sales and, correspondingly, no rationale for safety stocks.

Now if the reorder quantity q is set at 5 units, this control policy will mean that the inventory on hand fluctuates between a minimum of zero and a maximum of four and averages out to $(q - 1)/2 = 2$ units. The corresponding figure for the annual number of orders placed will be $D/q = {}^{25}\!/_{5} = 5$ orders.

In order to determine an optimal purchasing quantity, two conflicting cost components must be balanced against each other: inventory costs and ordering costs. The larger the warehouse sets q, the larger will be its average inventory, but the smaller will be the number of times at which it must incur the fixed costs of reordering. Average annual costs depend upon the order quantity q as follows:

$$
\begin{array}{c}
\text{Total} \\
\text{expected} \\
\text{annual} \\
\text{costs}
\end{array}
=
\begin{pmatrix}
\text{fixed} \\
\text{cost} \\
\text{of each} \\
\text{re-} \\
\text{order}
\end{pmatrix}
\begin{pmatrix}
\text{average} \\
\text{number} \\
\text{of} \\
\text{reorders} \\
\text{per year}
\end{pmatrix}
+
\begin{pmatrix}
\text{unit} \\
\text{annual} \\
\text{cost of} \\
\text{holding} \\
\text{inventory}
\end{pmatrix}
\begin{pmatrix}
\text{average} \\
\text{inven-} \\
\text{tory size}
\end{pmatrix}
$$

$$
\text{TEC}(q) = \quad a \quad\quad \frac{D}{q} \quad + \quad b \quad\quad \frac{q-1}{2} \qquad (8\text{-}4)
$$

Differentiating (8-4) with respect to the order quantity q and setting the derivative equal to zero,[1]

$$
\frac{d\text{TEC}(q)}{dq} = \frac{-aD}{q^2} + \frac{b}{2} = 0
$$

[1] The decision variable q (the number of tubes ordered) is obviously restricted to integer values. Despite this fact, much of our analysis will proceed as though the order quantity and the inventory level were continuous rather than discrete variables. Continuity will permit us to work with derivatives of the cost function rather than with the more awkward technique of finite differences.

Rearranging terms, this yields the traditional square-root EOQ formula:

$$q = \sqrt{\frac{2aD}{b}} \qquad (8\text{-}5)$$

Expression (8-5) yields highly intuitive results: There will be a larger reorder quantity whenever the annual demand or the fixed ordering costs are large or whenever the inventory-holding costs are low. For example, with fixed costs of $.10 for each order placed and with inventory costs of $.20 per tube-year to cover the return on working capital plus obsolescence and storage charges, the optimal order quantity would be

$$q = \sqrt{\frac{2aD}{b}} = \sqrt{\frac{2(.10)(25)}{.20}} = 5 \text{ tubes per order}$$

With these costs, in order to justify doubling the order quantity from 5 to 10 tubes, a *quadrupling* of annual demand would be required, from 25 to 100. One undisputed virtue of the EOQ model is that the optimal decision is highly insensitive to small errors in the input data.

Sequential decisions: Randomness in demand

With randomness in demand or in the timing of deliveries, this deterministic EOQ model seems pretty unpalatable. Assuming substantial penalties for shortages, it is a reasonable guess that the reorder point for the electronics warehouse should be considerably higher than the *average* demand during lead time. But how much higher? And what about the resulting interactions with the order size q? This is now a true sequential decision problem—one in which the optimal strategy no longer consists in placing a replenishment order at a specific future calendar date, but rather at a preselected future inventory position.[1]

---

[1] The following analysis of the problem is similar to that of T. Whitin, *Theory of Inventory Management*, Princeton University Press, Princeton, N.J., 1953, pp. 56–62.

Figure 8-4 suggests the basic characteristics of the random process under consideration. Demands are no longer spaced at exactly two-week intervals, but instead occur at random intervals anywhere between 0.5 and 3.5 weeks apart, an *average* interval of two weeks. Since this is supposed to be a stationary process with no short-run seasonal movements or long-run trends in demand, each reorder cycle is triggered off at exactly the same

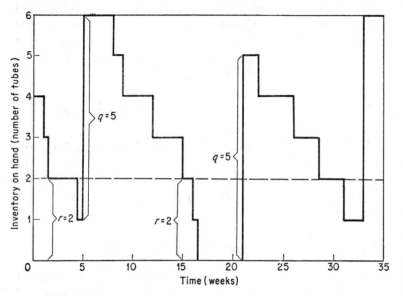

Fig. 8-4. A time series of inventory: randomness in demand.

reorder level r (in this diagram, $r = 2$). One such cycle begins at week 1.5, another at 15, and another at 28.5. Each order specifies the same delivery quantity q ($q = 5$) and restores the inventory level by this identical amount at the dates of replenishment: weeks 5, 21, and 33. Between week 16.5 and week 21, the item is out of stock, and shortages occur. Note that, because of randomness in delivery lags, the interval from the first reorder date to the first delivery date (the interval from week 1.5 to week 5) is of a different length from that for the second cycle (weeks 15 to 21) or for the third cycle (28.5 to 33).

In order for this picture of the inventory process to be valid, the following assumptions are made—assumptions made basically on grounds of analytical convenience rather than realism. In most practical applications, several of these restrictions would undoubtedly require modification:

(A) *The demand for tubes occurs one unit at a time. The time elapsing between each such demand is statistically independent*

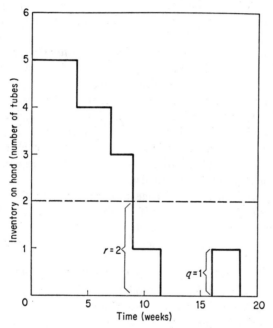

Fig. 8-5. A time series of inventory: violation of assumptions (A) and (C).

of its predecessor.[1]   This rules out the possibility of overshooting the reorder point, e.g., at week 9 in Figure 8-5.   In order to

---

[1] The Poisson distribution of demand during a fixed time span is one that will satisfy assumption (A).   (In the Poisson case, the interval between successive demands obeys a negative exponential density function.)   But there are other distributions that will also satisfy (A).   All that is required is the one-at-a-time property, plus independence of the interval between successive demands.

correct for overshooting, it would be necessary to change the order size from one cycle to the next. By contrast, on diagram 8-4, all replenishment orders are placed immediately when the inventory hits the reorder level r and are of the same magnitude, q.

(B) *The reorder quantity q is at least as large as the reorder point r.* This simplifies the analysis by eliminating the possible situation shown at week 16 in Figure 8-5. Despite replenishment at that time, the inventory level would never again get back to the reorder point of 2 units. No subsequent orders would ever get triggered off.

(C) *Only one replenishment order is outstanding at a time.* Assumptions (B) and (C) enable us to escape from the complications involved in multiple reorder point systems, e.g., ordering q_1 units when the inventory gets down to level r_1, then q_2 units when point r_2 is reached, and so on. Such multiplicity may, of course, be quite realistic but frequently leads to major complications in the analysis. Here it is guaranteed that each cycle will be triggered at a single reorder level r and that the replenishment order will always be the same size, q.

(D) *Demand during lead time is a random variable z with a known density function $p(z)$. If the demand z exceeds the reorder point stock level r, there will be lost sales amounting to the difference $(z - r)$. For each unit of lost sales, the warehouse incurs a shortage penalty cost of c.*

Assumption (D) is virtually identical with that used in the antifreeze peak seasonal demand model. In the present case, however, the peak occurs at each time the reorder point is reached, the only stage in the cycle at which a shortage can possibly occur.

This formulation allows directly for randomness in the timing of deliveries. The delivery time element can be compounded with the randomness of demand in defining the probability density function $p(z)$.

(E) *The reorder point r and reorder quantity q will be adjusted in such a way that the expected annual amount of unsatisfied demand is small in relation to D, the potential demand.*

Since the reorder quantity is identical from one cycle to the next, assumption (E) permits us to calculate the average number of order cycles per year as D/q, ignoring a minor correction for the fact that some demands will actually be lost and that the number of order cycles will be correspondingly reduced.

If assumptions (A) to (E) are satisfied, the components of average annual ordering and shortage costs may be written as follows:

$$\text{Ordering costs} = \left(\begin{array}{c}\text{ordering costs}\\ \text{per cycle}\end{array}\right)\left(\begin{array}{c}\text{expected number of}\\ \text{replenishment cycles}\\ \text{per year}\end{array}\right)$$

$$= a\left(\frac{D}{q}\right) \tag{8-6}$$

$$\text{Shortage costs} = \left(\begin{array}{c}\text{expected shortage}\\ \text{costs per cycle}\end{array}\right)\left(\begin{array}{c}\text{expected number of}\\ \text{replenishment cycles}\\ \text{per year}\end{array}\right)$$

$$= \left[c\int_{z=r}^{\infty}(z-r)p(z)\,dz\right]\left(\frac{D}{q}\right) \tag{8-7}$$

Average inventory costs are reckoned in this way:

If $0 \leq z \leq r$:

Ending inventory $= (r - z)$, with probability $p(z)\,dz$

If $r \leq z \leq \infty$:

Ending inventory $= 0$, with probability $\int_{z=r}^{\infty}p(z)\,dz$

Therefore

$$\text{Average ending inventory} = \int_{z=0}^{r}(r-z)p(z)\,dz$$
$$+ 0\int_{z=r}^{\infty}p(z)\,dz$$

Since the replenishment order is always of size q,

$$\text{Average inventory} = \frac{q}{2} + \int_{z=0}^{r}(r-z)p(z)\,dz$$

$$\text{Inventory costs} = \left(\begin{array}{c}\text{annual unit costs of}\\ \text{holding inventories}\end{array}\right)(\text{average inventory})$$

$$= b\left[\frac{q}{2} + \int_{z=0}^{r}(r-z)p(z)\,dz\right] \tag{8-8}$$

After the components listed in equations (8-6) to (8-8) are added, the total expected value of annual costs involved in ordering, in shortages, and in holding inventory can be written as a function of both decision variables, the reorder point and the reorder quantity:

$$\text{TEC}(q,r) = \left[a + c \int_{z=r}^{\infty} (z - r)p(z)\, dz \right]\left(\frac{D}{q}\right)$$
$$+ b\left[\frac{q}{2} + \int_{z=0}^{r} (r - z)p(z)\, dz \right] \quad (8\text{-}9)$$

Differentiating partially with respect to q and r, setting the results equal to zero, and rearranging terms,[1]

$$\int_{z=r}^{\infty} p(z)\, dz = \frac{b}{b + c\,(D/q)} \quad (8\text{-}10)$$

and
$$q = \sqrt{\frac{2D\left[a + c \int_{z=r}^{\infty} (z - r)p(z)\, dz \right]}{b}} \quad (8\text{-}11)$$

These two conditions closely resemble those worked out previously for the two simpler models upon which this one was based. Equation (8-11) is similar to the square-root EOQ formula calculated for the completely deterministic case in (8-5). The expected cost of shortages during a replenishment cycle now acts to increase the optimum order size q in just the same way as does an increase in the ordering costs, a. Unlike the previous lot-size model, here the ordering quantity q depends intimately upon the size of the reorder point r. Neither r nor q can be determined independently. Both (8-10) and (8-11) must be solved simultaneously, by iterative means if necessary.

Equation (8-10) is highly reminiscent of the optimal safety stock required for the peak-season inventory problem. Like equation (8-3), this one says that the safety stock r should be

[1] A reminder on one technical point: According to assumption (B), we are entitled to differentiate independently with respect to q and r if, and only if, (8-10) and (8-11) happen to turn out so that $q \geq r$. If they do not work out this way, assumption (B) forces us to set $q = r$ and to reoptimize (8-9) under this side condition.

of such a size as to give a shortage probability equal to the ratio
between annual costs per unit of inventory and the total of unit
inventory costs plus the annual rate for shortage penalties.

Conditions (8-10) and (8-11) do *not* provide an all-purpose
solution to inventory problems. In attempting to apply such a
model, the reader should constantly keep in mind the very restrictive conditions upon which this model is based: absence of trend
and seasonality, infinite-time horizon, no competition with other
items for limited productive capacity, linear costs, and continuous
possibilities of reordering—as well as the assumptions spelled out
explicitly in (A) to (E). This particular formulation represents
only one out of a large number of conceivably acceptable ideal-
izations of inventory processes. The reader should realize that
with this model, as with all others presented in this volume, he is
not apt to come across a real-world problem for which the formula is already written down. Instead he should have a sufficiently full understanding of the assumptions and the analytical
techniques so that he will be prepared to construct a model appropriate to the actual, rather than the textbook, situation.

EXERCISES[1]

8-1. Refer back to the Apollo Antifreeze cost function, equation (8-1). Construct $\text{TEC}(x)$ as a function of x for three
alternative levels of the shortage penalty c: \$.40, \$1, and \$4.
How much of a departure from the *minimum* attainable level
of total costs would occur if the parameter c had been estimated
at \$1 and its true value were \$.40? What if its true value had
been \$4?

8-2. In designing a chemical plant, the process engineering
group finds that, if a certain pump breaks down and no spare is
available, the entire plant will be idle for a day. The plant's

---

[1] A word to the statistically sophisticated reader: Any data cited in these
exercises are to be regarded as coming from a large rather than a small sample. You may disregard the very important distinction between relative
frequencies in a finite- and an infinite-size sample.

daily output is valued at $75,000. A shutdown would mean, however, a saving in raw materials and power of $25,000 during the repair period.

This kind of pump is likely to break down on one day out of ten. Two pumps, with independent breakdown probabilities, would imply a plant shutdown one out of every hundred days, and so on. Each additional pump will involve extra initial costs plus operating costs of $400 a year. How many pumps can be afforded in the initial design? Is it possible to add enough redundancy so that these pumps will *never* cause a plant shutdown?

8-3. The following represents a 40-month time series of predicted and actual demand for a certain brand of soap:[1]

Month	Predicted	Actual	Month	Predicted	Actual
1	155	180	21	270	209
2	203	147	22	200	193
3	242	207	23	130	88
4	230	203	24	170	128
5	169	123	25	140	67
6	210	155	26	130	120
7	157	167	27	160	100
8	158	148	28	150	121
9	313	303	29	225	238
10	275	319	30	140	124
11	128	126	31	170	169
12	133	57	32	328	451
13	235	254	33	120	62
14	190	119	34	165	93
15	170	68	35	215	146
16	160	84	36	140	120
17	200	199	37	230	103
18	235	206	38	230	271
19	100	66	39	175	148
20	140	120	40	215	173

[1] These are historical figures furnished by one producer.

Do you detect any kind of systematic forecasting error here? The current prediction of the marketing department is that, because of a special promotional effort, next month's demand will jump to 450. There will be no inventory carried forward to assist in meeting this peak. The marginal costs of straight-time production are constant at $300 up to a monthly production capacity of 700 units. Thereafter, because of the time-and-a-half shift premium for overtime work, marginal costs will become $450. An inventory cost of $100 will be incurred for each unit of month-end inventory.

The straight-time production rate must be set at the beginning of the month and kept constant throughout the period. Overtime, however, can be ordered at any point. Shortages will not be permitted to occur. Any excess demand will be handled by overtime. At what rate should the straight-time production be set?

8-4. The Ajax Steel Company owns a finishing mill engaged in the conversion of steel billets into bars.[1] The standard length for finished bars is 40 feet. Because of variations in processing conditions, it is necessary to adjust the mean billet size so as to roll a slightly over-sized hot bar, and then, after cooling, to cut the bar down to the 40-foot standard length. Any excess that is trimmed away is useless except for scrap.

A cold bar that turns out to be less than 40 feet is also useless and must be utilized as scrap. Given the following frequency distribution around the mean length of cold bars, find the mean length that will minimize the total scrap loss. Is the Ajax Company wise in marketing just the 40-foot standard-size bar?

This table is to be read as follows: If the mean length is set at, say, 41 feet, 1 per cent of the resulting bars will actually turn out to be 38 feet, 3 feet smaller than the mean; 4 per cent will be 39 feet; etc.

[1] Example adapted from one described by S. Eilon and B. Avi-Itzhak, "Case Study in the Rolling of Steel Bars," *Journal of Mechanical Engineering Science,* vol. 2, no. 2, 1960.

Deviation from mean length of bars (feet):

$$-3 \quad -2 \quad -1 \quad 0 \quad +1 \quad +2 \quad +3$$

Probability of given deviation:

$$.01 \quad .04 \quad .20 \quad .50 \quad .20 \quad .04 \quad .01$$

8-5. The demand history of a certain item over the past 40 weeks can be summarized as follows:

Number of demands	Number of weeks
0	25
1	10
2	5

Two out of every three replenishment orders have taken a week to be filled; the remainder, two weeks. Derive the probability of a shortage for all possible values of the reorder point.

8-6. An Air Force base estimates that its average annual demand for a certain item is 10 units, and the demand during routine replenishment lead time has the following density function: $p(z) = e^{-z}$.

It costs $20 for bookkeeping and handling at the base and depot level for each order that is placed, regardless of order size. Inventory costs may be taken at $100 per year for each unit of inventory held. In the event that the base stock on hand is insufficient to meet demand, a high-priority requisition will be placed in order to cover the deficit. On the average, the high-priority replenishment will be received within two days.

There is some disagreement over the extent of the weapon system that will be put out of commission because of lack of this particular item. Some officers believe that a temporary shortage would have no effect upon the capabilities of the system. Others argue that a shortage would idle a system worth $50 per day. Still others argue that the extent of damage would be worse: $250 per day for the system.

To the nearest tenth of a unit, what would be the optimal levels of the reorder point and reorder quantity for this item? How many shortages a year would correspond to your recommendations? Do your calculation for each of the three implied levels of the shortage penalty.

Hint. $$\int ze^{-z}\,dz = -e^{-z}(1+z)$$

8-7. In an effort to reduce working-capital requirements, it has been decided that the working capital employed by a machine shop is to be cut down to an *average* of \$35,000. Cost, working-capital, and sales information on the three stock items carried are as follows:

Product	Annual sales rate, units	Costs per setup,* dollars	Working capital required per unit stocked, dollars
A	225	1,000	100
B	150	1,000	150
C	400	2,000	200

* These setup costs are incurred once each production run, regardless of the length of the run.

Keeping in mind the over-all limitation upon working capital, recommend run lengths for each of the three products.

Hint. Find an implicit worth of capital that restricts demand within the availability of \$35,000.

CHAPTER NINE

DYNAMIC PROGRAMMING—
INVENTORY CONTROL

Recursive optimality: A game example

After examining the extensive list of restrictive assumptions involved in setting up the preceding inventory models, the reader is entitled to be discouraged. In this chapter, a more general approach will be examined: dynamic programming, which makes it possible to dispense with many of these unrealistic restrictions and at the same time does not entail an inordinate amount of calculation. "Dynamic programming" is the term coined by Richard Bellman[1] to characterize the joint application of two ideas: (1) recursive optimality and (2) summarization in terms of a "state variable."

The notion of recursive optimality can be illustrated by the following parlor game, the compound lottery of Figure 9-1: This game involves several alternations between the player's moves (solid lines) and chance moves (dotted lines). The probabilities of these chance moves are known in advance to the player and are indicated in parentheses above the dotted lines. The game

[1] R. Bellman, *Dynamic Programming*, Princeton University Press, Princeton, N.J., 1957.

begins at point A and ends when the player has reached one of the terminal points D, E, F, K, L, M, or N with respective prizes of $10, $2, etc. At the initial point A, the player has the right to choose the upper subgame at B or the lower subgame at C. If he chooses B, a fair coin will be tossed, and with a 50-50 probability, he will move to the final state D with a prize of $10 or to point E with $2. If, instead, the player initially chooses C,

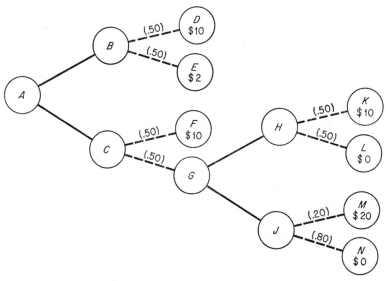

Fig. 9-1. A compound lottery game.

there is a 50-50 chance that he will end up in state F with $10 or in state G with the option of proceeding to either subgame H or subgame J. From H, there is a 50-50 chance that the player will terminate at point K ($10 prize) or at point L ($0 prize). And from J, there is a 20 per cent chance of reaching the big $20 prize at point M and an 80 per cent chance of zero at N.

In order to analyze all this, it is necessary to agree to some specific assumption about the way in which our hypothetical player decides between alternatives under conditions of risk. Both for present purposes and for dynamic programming analyses of business decisions, it will be supposed that the player evaluates the game solely in terms of *expected* gains and losses. He does not possess a do-or-die temperament and is not determined to get the $20 prize at all costs. He is not a timid soul, convinced that luck always runs against him and that he had better play safe by choosing alternative B with its guaranteed minimum return of $2. He will, for example, attach a $4 valuation to the subgame indicated at point J:

$$\$4 = \begin{pmatrix} \text{probability of} \\ \text{ending in } M \end{pmatrix} \begin{pmatrix} \text{prize} \\ \text{at } M \end{pmatrix} + \begin{pmatrix} \text{probability of} \\ \text{ending in } N \end{pmatrix} \begin{pmatrix} \text{prize} \\ \text{at } N \end{pmatrix}$$
$$= \quad (.20) \qquad (\$20) \ + \qquad (.80) \qquad (\$0)$$

The player knows that the money value of the game is small enough so that in the event of either victory or defeat, his total assets will not be greatly altered. The expected money value criterion is clearly unwarranted in many gambling situations and would be inappropriate for most individuals contemplating self-insurance on their own automobiles or homes. It would be still less appropriate as a guide for stock-market decisions by an elderly coupon clipper or as a guide for a major plant-expansion decision by a small illiquid enterprise.[1] In most of these cases, a prudent decision maker is willing to pay a small premium (or to incur a small loss) in order to insure against a catastrophic outcome. But when it comes to such matters as routine inventory decisions or *small* investments or parlor games, the decision maker can afford to take advantage of the law of large numbers, pooling together many individual independent risks; this is where the expected money value criterion comes into its own.

Now back to our hypothetical game player: It has already been seen that he assigns an expected value of $4 to position J, and this valuation is indicated in the new diagram (Figure 9-2). By similar reasoning, he works back from the terminal values at positions K and L to assign a $5 value to point H. With this information, it is easy to evaluate position G. From here, he

---

[1] There is a readable discussion of these matters in H. Markowitz, *Portfolio Selection*, John Wiley & Sons, Inc., New York, 1959, chaps. 11–13.

will prefer moving forward to the adjacent point H ($5 expected value) instead of moving to J with its $4 value. This establishes a value of $5 for position G.

Knowing that F is a terminal state with a value of $10 and G an intermediate state worth $5, he derives the value of $7.50 for position C. Working backward from D and E, he calculates $6 for B. And when at A, he is faced with a choice between

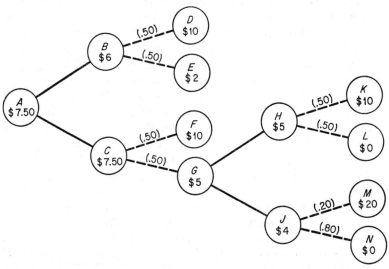

Fig. 9-2. Evaluation of the compound lottery.

moving to a $6 or a $7.50 position, the choice is clear-cut. From A, the player would move to C, and so position A is worth $7.50.

Now that he has moved backward through the problem, he knows how to move forward. From position A, for example, the player looks only at the two adjacent positions B and C. He does not need to examine explicitly all the terminal states D, E, F, etc., nor all the paths leading to these states. Instead, the valuation of each intermediate state summarizes the whole picture for him and permits him to take one step at a time, knowing that all further moves have been optimally planned. In Bell-

man's words: "An optimal policy has the property that whatever
the initial state and initial decision are, the remaining decisions
must constitute an optimal policy with respect to the state
resulting from the first decision."[1]

Application to inventory control

Recursive optimality, although a powerful-looking concept,
loses much of its attractiveness unless it can be coupled to
another feature: description of the system in terms of a *small*
number of states.   In Figure 9-1, for example, there are only two
states, A and G, at which the player is required to make a
decision.   If, instead, each decision move led to 10 alternative
chance moves and each chance move to 10 alternative decision
points, a game with just 10 moves of each type would imply an
astronomical number of states.   In the last set of a player's
moves, there would be 100^9 states.   Even a computer capable of
finding an optimal decision for each state in one-millionth of a
second would take almost 32 thousand years of uninterrupted
time to calculate the last move!

The inventory problem lends itself to dynamic programming
just because the state of the system can ordinarily be measured
in terms of a manageable number of states, frequently in terms
of the single state variable: (quantity of inventory on hand.)
Provided that we are concerned with the case of a single
stock item at a single location and with a single replenishment
lag, there will be just one state for each time period and inventory level.   Once a particular inventory level and point in time
are set, the optimal policy thereafter is identical, regardless of the
entire previous history of demands and of replenishments.   A
multi-item, multi-location, or multi-lag problem can also be
analyzed by the same principles, using additional dimensions,
but only at the cost of a substantial increase in computing
effort.

The standard approach to the inventory problem runs something like this: Once each "period," an enterprise examines its

[1] R. Bellman, *op. cit.,* p. 83.

inventory position on a certain item.   On the basis of this
position, the enterprise decides how much of the item, if any, to
order for stock replenishment.   The replenishment order arrives
in sufficient time to meet demand of the current period.   As in
the cases discussed in the preceding chapter, it will be assumed
that any excess of demand over the available inventory results in
a shortage and a corresponding penalty cost.   Also as in those
cases, it will be assumed that the firm aims at minimizing the
expected total of ordering costs, shortage costs, and inventory
costs.

Unlike the previous chapter, the criterion here consists of
minimizing the *present value* rather than the average value of
these costs.   An even more significant departure: The firm is no
longer permitted the option of ordering at any continuous point
in time, but only at discrete intervals, once each period.   (It is
especially realistic to assume discrete ordering intervals if the
individual item is one of a large number being shipped at the
same time, e.g., on a weekly truck.)   This assumption of dis-
creteness makes it possible to abandon the previous restrictive
assumptions (A), (B), and (E) of Chapter 8.   We shall still
require (C) and (D).   There will still be only one replenishment
order outstanding at a time.[1]   It will still be assumed that the
distribution of demand during each lead time period is an independently distributed random variable with a known probability
distribution.   And it will still be assumed that, if the demand
exceeds the stock available, there will be lost sales amounting to
the difference between these two quantities.

A small-scale illustration of such a problem is shown in Figure
9-3, a case in which the inventory position is reviewed once each
year.   The Delphic Computer Company is due to shift over to a
new type of computer at the end of two years.   Meanwhile, the

---

[1] For an alternative formulation—one that allows for the possibility of a
replenishment lag and also several outstanding orders—see S. Karlin and
H. Scarf, "Inventory Models of the Arrow-Harris-Marschak Type with
Time Lag," in K. Arrow, S. Karlin, and H. Scarf (eds.), *Studies in the
Mathematical Theory of Inventory and Production*, Stanford University Press,
Stanford, 1958, chap. 10.

company is faced with the problem of establishing an inventory policy with respect to magnetic drums for repair purposes on its existing model. These drums will be completely obsolete at the end of two years, and salvage values at that point will be negligible. (Zero values in the three right-hand terminal states in

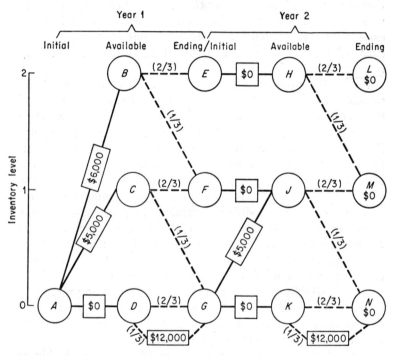

Fig. 9-3. Delphic inventory problem.

Figure 9-3). The distr bution of demand for spare drums during each of the next two years is identically and independently distributed: a ⅔ probability of zero and a ⅓ probability of one demand.

Starting with a current inventory of zero, this demand pattern means that there are three possible values for the inventory controller's initial move: order zero, one, or two units. Next comes a random move, a first-year demand for either zero or one unit. (A shortage occurs only if zero is ordered and one unit is demanded.) The random move, together with the previous ordering decision, determines the ending inventory for the first year and, simultaneously, the initial inventory for the second.

On the basis of this initial inventory for the second year, the controller decides whether or not to place an additional drum in stock, and a chance move determines the magnitude of the shortage, if any, and the terminal inventory. If this were a three-period model, the ending inventory for the second period would constitute the initial position for the third one, etc.

The Delphic Company is concerned with three types of costs: ordering costs, shortage costs, and interest plus obsolescence. Interest and obsolescence are incorporated through a present-worth factor. Using the value of .75 for the factor, this means that $1,000 worth of ordering or shortage costs incurred during the second year has an expected present value of only $750 during the first year. This factor is intended to account not only for the return on capital tied up in any cash outlays but also for the probability of obsolescence at the end of the first year, i.e., the probability that the second year's expenses will not actually be incurred.

The shortage penalty costs are taken to be $12,000 per shortage. Since the probability of a one-unit demand is $\frac{1}{3}$, the expected current cost of shortages is $4,000 whenever zero spare drums are in the available inventory, and is zero otherwise.

Because of setup and handling costs, it will be assumed that there are economies in placing large-scale orders. The total costs versus size of order are indicated below and also in the boxes along the solid lines of Figure 9-3.

Size of order	Current ordering costs
0	$ 0
1	$5,000
2	$6,000

Inventory control: Recursive optimality

Figure 9-4 demonstrates the application of recursive optimality to this numerical example. Just as in the compound lottery, we work backward from the values attached to the terminal states, taking account now of the shortage and procurement costs indicated in the various boxes.

First to be evaluated are the availability levels for the second year (positions *H*, *J*, and *K*). With an availability level of

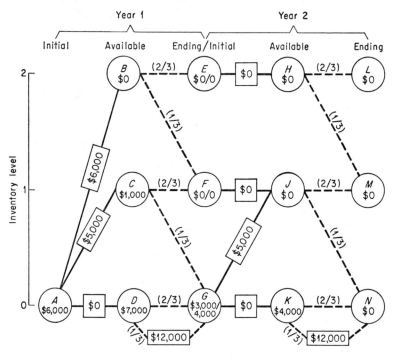

Fig. 9-4. Evaluation of the Delphic inventory problem.

either one or two drums, there is no possibility of a shortage, and so expected future costs are zero at *H* and *J*; but with zero spares available (position *K*), the expected shortages will cost $4,000.

From *H*, *J*, and *K*, we can work backward to the initial inventory positions for the second year (*E*, *F*, and *G*). At positions *E* and *F*, the obvious course of action is to order zero. Future costs associated with those two positions will be zero. In position G, however, there is a choice to be made: either a one-unit order at a cost of \$5,000 and a move to position J with zero subsequent costs, or else a zero order, zero direct costs, and a move to position K with subsequent costs of \$4,000. The minimum-cost move is obviously the latter, and so this establishes a \$4,000 value for the second year's costs at position G.

Now in order for this \$4,000 value to be comparable with costs incurred during the first period, we apply the present-worth factor of .75. This leads to the initial figure of \$3,000 shown in circle G, the *present* value of the second year's costs, ending the first year with an inventory position of zero.

From the first year's ending positions, from the shortage cost between D and G, and from the demand probabilities, the inventory availability levels B, C, and D can be evaluated. For example, the future cost of \$1,000 inserted in circle C results from the following calculation:

$$\$1,000 = \begin{pmatrix} \text{proba-} \\ \text{bility of} \\ \text{moving} \\ \text{to posi-} \\ \text{tion } F \end{pmatrix} \begin{pmatrix} \text{ex-} \\ \text{pected} \\ \text{future} \\ \text{costs} \\ \text{in } F \end{pmatrix} + \begin{pmatrix} \text{proba-} \\ \text{bility of} \\ \text{moving} \\ \text{to posi-} \\ \text{tion } G \end{pmatrix} \begin{pmatrix} \text{ex-} \\ \text{pected} \\ \text{future} \\ \text{costs} \\ \text{in } G \end{pmatrix}$$

$$= \quad (\tfrac{2}{3}) \quad\quad (\$0) \quad + \quad (\tfrac{1}{3}) \quad\quad (\$3,000)$$

And from the initial position A, there are three choices: a move to B with ordering costs of \$6,000 and subsequent costs of zero; a move to C with ordering costs of \$5,000 and subsequent costs of \$1,000; or a move to D with zero ordering costs and subsequent costs of \$7,000. The minimum level of future costs from A onward is \$6,000—a cost level attained by ordering either one or two units. Either of these two actions is equally good. There is a substantial penalty involved in the third alternative, an initial order of size zero. This nonoptimal initial action would result in future costs of \$7,000 even if an optimal policy were pursued in the second year.

Dynamic programming: The functional equation

With more realistic problems extending over many time periods and inventory levels, the identical principle is applicable: working backward from each state to its immediate predecessor and taking account of the expected value of all costs incurred en route. Such flow diagrams as Figure 9-4 can be summarized in the following relationship, known as a functional equation. This type of equation is one in which a function, $v_i{}^t$, is regarded as the unknown to be found:

Minimum
expected
present
value of   minimum   ⌈current   current
all future   with   procure-   shortage
costs,   respect   ment   costs, a   ⎛pres-⎞   ⎛proba-⎞   ⎛minimum   expected⎞
starting   = to the   costs, a   function   +   ⎜ent- ⎟ (∑) ⎜bility⎟   ⎜present value of all⎟
from an   order   function   of the   ⎝wcrth⎠   ⎜of   ⎟   ⎜future costs at time⎟
initial   quantity   of the   avail-   ⎝factor⎠   ⎜demand⎟   ⎜$t+1$, starting from an⎟
inventory q order   ability   ⎜for z⎟ ⎜initial inventory of⎟
of i ⌊size q level   ⎝units ⎠   ⎜either $i+q-z$ or zero,⎟
units at $i+q$ ⎝whichever is larger ⎠
time t

$$v_i{}^t = \min_{q \geq 0} \left(\begin{array}{l} C_1{}^t(q) + C_2{}^t(i+q) + \alpha \sum_{z < i+q} p_z{}^t v_{i+q-z}{}^{t+1} \\[2mm] \qquad\qquad\qquad\quad + \alpha \sum_{z \geq i+q} p_z{}^t v_0{}^{t+1} \end{array} \right) \qquad (9\text{-}1)$$

Relationship (9-1) says that, for each possible inventory level i at time t, we are to establish an optimal order quantity q and a corresponding value $v_i{}^t$, choosing q in such a way as to minimize the sum of current procurement costs, current shortage costs, and the discounted expected future costs, following an optimal policy from time $t+1$ onward. In this way, the functional equation shows us how to calculate the position values $v_i{}^t$, given the current cost functions $C_1{}^t(q)$ and $C_2{}^t(i+q)$ and the subsequent value schedule $v_i{}^{t+1}$.

Since each of the cost functions and probabilities has a time superscript t, this formulation allows for the possibility that the costs and probabilities will shift in a known fashion from one period to the next. Procurement costs and shortage costs for each point in time are assumed to be a part of the initial data.

If shortage costs just depend upon the expected number of shortages, this expected number can be determined in the same way as the right-hand component of equation (8-1) in the preceding chapter, replacing the density function $p(z)$ by discrete probabilities $p_z{}^t$, for time t, and replacing integrals by sums:

$$\text{Expected number of shortages} = \sum_{z \geq i+q} p_z{}^t(z - i - q) \quad (9\text{-}2)$$

Now *if* we have already learned what value schedule to attach to initial inventories at time $t + 1$, the rest is easy. With probability $p_z{}^t$, demand will take on the value of z units. If $z < i + q$, the ending inventory for period t will be a positive amount: $i + q - z$. But if $z \geq i + q$, there will be a certain amount of unsatisfied demand, and ending inventories will be zero. Together, the two final terms in (9-1) establish the expected value of the initial inventory for period $t + 1$ and discount this value back to period t by the present-worth factor α.

When inspected closely, it turns out that, for a fixed value of the state variable i, the formidable expression within the brackets on the right-hand side of (9-1) depends upon the decision variable q alone. Through direct enumeration, as in the Delphic Computer example, or by more sophisticated means,[1] the functional equation instructs us to find a value of q that minimizes the sum of present and future costs starting from an inventory position of i units. Once the schedule $v_i{}^t$ has been determined, equation (9-1) tells us how to construct the schedule $v_i{}^{t-1}$. From this, in turn, follows $v_i{}^{t-2}, v_i{}^{t-3}. \ . \ . \ .$ All that is needed is a starting point, a schedule of terminal inventory values at some cutoff date in the future. With such a schedule of terminal values and with demand distributions and cost functions for each point in time, the rest is just a matter of arithmetic to determine a particular set of optimal policies and minimum costs.

But what if there is no natural cutoff date inherent in the problem? What if, for example, we were managing inventories of

---

[1] See R. Bellman, *op. cit.*, pp. 159–164. For a statement of conditions under which it is optimal to pursue a simple reorder point policy, see H. Scarf, "The Optimality of S, s Policies in the Dynamic Inventory Problem," in K. Arrow, S. Karlin, and P. Suppes (eds.), *Mathematical Methods in the Social Sciences, 1959*, Stanford University Press, Stanford, 1960.

heating oil or of hydroelectric energy? Any specific cutoff date and set of salvage values would be rather arbitrary in the case of these commodities. Not only may an infinite time horizon be a more satisfactory idealization than a finite one, but also, in comparison with certain cases involving many time periods, the numerical analysis turns out to be easier. Interestingly enough, it then becomes possible to apply a probabilistic form of linear programming.[1]

Linear programming for the infinite-horizon case

In the infinite-horizon case, it is easiest to suppose that we are dealing with identical cost functions, identical discount factors, and identical probability distributions from one period to the next over the indefinite future. (Through a comparatively minor modification, it is quite feasible to handle the case of repetitive seasonal variations in these elements. See exercise 9-5.) For this infinite-horizon case, we are concerned with finding values v_i that satisfy the functional equation (9-1), omitting all time superscripts t. Note that the unknowns v_i now appear on both sides of the equation:

$$v_i = \min_{q \geq 0} \left\{ \begin{matrix} C_1(q) + C_2(i + q) + \alpha \sum_{z < i+q} p_z v_{i+q-z} \\ + \alpha \sum_{z \geq i+q} p_z v_0 \end{matrix} \right\} \quad (9\text{-}3)$$

First comes the question: Does there exist a finite-valued set of v_i that will satisfy (9-3)? Not always. Suppose that we are dealing with a trivial problem in which it is always cheaper to incur the shortage penalty rather than to order any positive quantity q. Then, according to (9-3) we are looking for a value v_0 such that

$$v_0 = C_2(0) + \alpha v_0 \quad (9\text{-}4)$$

If there are any shortage penalties at all, i.e., if $C_2(0) > 0$ and if $\alpha \geq 1$, infinity is the only value of v_0 that will satisfy (9-4).

[1] This linear programming formulation was developed by F. d'Epenoux, "Sur un problème de production et de stockage dans l'aléatoire," *Revue française de recherche opérationnelle*, no. 14, 1960.

In searching for a set of finite v_i, then, we shall always assume that α lies between the following very reasonable limits: $0 < \alpha < 1$.

Even if the discount factor lies between these bounds, there is likely to be trouble unless we place some additional restrictions upon the problem: (1) We shall suppose that the quantities i, q, and z—respectively, inventory levels, order quantities, and demand quantities—are nonnegative integers. (2) For finite values of i and q, the procurement and shortage cost functions take on finite nonnegative values. (3) There exists a positive integer I, an upper limit upon inventory accumulation. For any specific i, this implies that the choice of q is bounded between the following limits:

$$0 \le q \le I - i \qquad (9\text{-}5)$$

By condition 3, both i and q must be finite. By condition 2, there is a finite maximum, denoted $C_{\max}$, to the procurement and shortage costs incurred during any specific time period. Define $v_{\max}$ as the maximum among the quantities $v_0, v_1, \ldots, v_I$. Then by (9-3) and by the fact that $\sum_z p_z = 1$:

$$v_{\max} \le C_{\max} + \alpha v_{\max}$$

Therefore
$$v_{\max} \le \frac{C_{\max}}{1 - \alpha} < \infty \qquad (9\text{-}6)$$

Equation (9-6) proves that there exists a set of finite-valued v_i that will satisfy the functional equation (9-3). By similar reasoning, it can be proved that the v_i are nonnegative. But how can numerical values for the v_i be obtained? This is where linear programming comes in. From (9-3), we are entitled to write the following set of linear inequalities, one for each admissible combination of i and q:

$$v_i \le C_1(q) + C_2(i + q) + \alpha \sum_{z < i+q} p_z v_{i+q-z}$$
$$+ \alpha \sum_{z \ge i+q} p_z v_0 \qquad i \text{ and } q \colon 0 \le q \le I - i \quad (9\text{-}7)$$

The linear programming problem consists of assigning nonnegative values to the v_i in such a way as to satisfy (9-7) and also maximize the following expression:[1]

Maximize $$\sum_{i=0}^{I} v_i \qquad (9\text{-}8)$$

To maximize (9-8) is surely a curious way to go about performing the minimization specified by the functional equation (9-3). Minimization by maximization? But it really does make sense. Consider the problem of finding the minimum of the three integers: 3, 7, 4. We could write this problem in a form resembling a functional equation:

$$v = \min (3, 7, 4)$$

Or, alternatively, we could write this as a linear programming problem:

Maximize v

subject to:

$$v \leq 3$$
$$v \leq 7$$
$$v \leq 4$$
$$v \geq 0$$

In either form, the solution is $v = 3$. In the form of a functional equation, we put things in a straightforward way and say that we are looking for the minimum of these three numbers. In the linear programming case, we do something devious and say that we are looking for their *greatest* lower bound. Both are equally legitimate ways of looking at the same operation.

For a numerical illustration of the linear programming approach, let us use the data from the Delphic Computer inventory problem. As before, we shall suppose that there is an upper limit of 2 units upon inventory accumulation ($I = 2$). The same procurement and shortage cost data will be employed. Also the same discount factor and probability distribution of demand

---

[1] We could also take as our maximand the more general expression $\sum_{i=0}^{I} \beta_i v_i$, where the coefficients β_i represent any arbitrary positive weights.

will be used.   The only difference is that, since this is an infinite-horizon situation, we ignore the terminal value schedule used previously.   (This schedule was not very interesting anyway: a zero salvage value for each computer drum left over.)   Any such infinite-horizon problem leads to a total of $(I + 2)(I + 1)/2$ inequality restrictions in the $I + 1$ unknowns.[1]   Here there are six inequalities with three unknowns:

Maximize $$v_0 + v_1 + v_2$$

subject to

$$v_i \leq C_1(q) + C_2(i + q) + \text{discounted future costs}$$

$$i = 0 \quad \begin{aligned} v_0 &\leq 0 + 4{,}000 + .75(v_0) & q &= 0 \\ v_0 &\leq 5{,}000 + 0 + .75(\tfrac{2}{3}v_1 + \tfrac{1}{3}v_0) & q &= 1 \\ v_0 &\leq 6{,}000 + 0 + .75(\tfrac{2}{3}v_2 + \tfrac{1}{3}v_1) & q &= 2 \end{aligned} \quad (9\text{-}9)$$

$$i = 1 \quad \begin{aligned} v_1 &\leq 0 + 0 + .75(\tfrac{2}{3}v_1 + \tfrac{1}{3}v_0) & q &= 0 \\ v_1 &\leq 5{,}000 + 0 + .75(\tfrac{2}{3}v_2 + \tfrac{1}{3}v_1) & q &= 1 \end{aligned}$$

$$i = 2 \quad v_2 \leq 0 + 0 + .75(\tfrac{2}{3}v_2 + \tfrac{1}{3}v_1) \qquad q = 0$$

and $$v_i \geq 0$$

The optimal solution is unique in the v_i:

$$v_0 = 8{,}000 \qquad v_1 = 4{,}000 \qquad v_2 = 2{,}000$$

Inserting these values into the six restrictions listed above:

$$i = 0 \quad \begin{aligned} v_0 &= 8{,}000 \leq 10{,}000 & q &= 0 & (9\text{-}10) \\ v_0 &= 8{,}000 \leq 9{,}000 & q &= 1 & (9\text{-}10a) \\ v_0 &= 8{,}000 \leq 8{,}000 & q &= 2 & (9\text{-}10b) \end{aligned}$$

$$i = 1 \quad \begin{aligned} v_1 &= 4{,}000 \leq 4{,}000 & q &= 0 & (9\text{-}11) \\ v_1 &= 4{,}000 \leq 7{,}000 & q &= 1 & (9\text{-}11a) \end{aligned}$$

$$i = 2 \quad v_2 = 2{,}000 \leq 2{,}000 \qquad q = 0 \qquad (9\text{-}12)$$

Now that the valuation schedule has been established, how are we to read off an optimal replenishment policy, the quantities,

[1] For practical computations, it is convenient to solve such problems by the dual simplex method.   See S. Gass, *Linear Programming*, McGraw-Hill Book Company, Inc., New York, 1958, chap. 5 and pp. 125–130.   Through the dual method, the computational job can be reduced to a problem involving just $I + 1$ restrictions.

if any, to be ordered at each inventory level? Among the restrictions numbered (9-10) to (9-10b), those corresponding to a zero initial inventory, there is just one for which the right- and left-hand sides are equal. This restriction is (9-10b), the one corresponding to the action of ordering two units. By definition of the functional equation (9-3), this equality means that the action of ordering two units is the one that will lead to minimum costs. And in general, whenever we find a restriction holding with an equality rather than an inequality, the corresponding action is optimal.[1] The decision rule produced here is the following one. It can be verified that this strategy coincides with an optimal initial policy for the two-period finite-horizon case.

By (9-10b)   Whenever $i = 0$, optimal $q = 2$
By (9-11)   Whenever $i = 1$, optimal $q = 0$
By (9-12)   Whenever $i = 2$, optimal $q = 0$

EXERCISES

9-1. The linear programming model described by conditions (9-9) was based upon a shortage penalty of $12,000 per unit. Within what limits could this shortage penalty vary and the optimal solution remain unchanged? What would be the result if the shortage penalty fell outside these limits?

9-2. Go back to Figure 9-3, the two-period finite-horizon case. Recalculate the optimal solution under the assumption that there will be a current salvage value of $300 for each computer drum on hand at the end of the second year. (*Caution:* The salvage value is a credit, not a cost.)

9-3. Use the principle of recursive optimality to solve the Titanic Chemical Corporation capacity expansion problem presented at the end of Chapter 6. Interpret your state variable not as inventory, but as demand minus previously installed capacity.

---

[1] For a given inventory level, there may be several restrictions holding with an equality sign. This just means that the optimal course of action is not unique. The valuations v_i, however, will always be unique.

9-4. A petroleum company is concerned with establishing an optimal production and inventory policy to deal with seasonal fluctuations in the demand for heating oil over the two following seasons. The probability distribution of demand during each of these seasons is:

Summer season		Winter season	
Demand, millions of barrels	Probability of demand	Demand, millions of barrels	Probability of demand
5	.5	20	⅓
10	.5	25	⅓
		30	⅓

At the beginning of each season, the company examines its inventory position and then sets a production rate which remains constant throughout the season. Any shortages will be made good through supplementary purchases on the open market at the exorbitant price of $6 a barrel. Any inventories on hand at the end of the winter season will be credited at the rate of $3 a barrel. The company's production costs vary with the season of the year and the total quantity produced. The higher the production rate, the more expensive will be the materials employed for heating oil purposes:

Production rate for season	Total costs, millions of dollars	
	Summer season	Winter season
5	15	15
10	30	30
15	45	45
20	60	60
25	75	80
30	90	100

There is seasonal storage capacity for no more than 10 million barrels. Production rates for each season must be adjusted to the initial inventory so that the ending level will never exceed the storage capacity. The only production rates to be considered will be multiples of 5 million barrels, namely, 5, 10, 15, 20, 25, and 30. Each season's costs are discounted by a factor of .90 to arrive at present worth during the preceding season.

Assuming a zero initial inventory for the summer period, what policy will result in minimum costs during that period and the following winter?   What benefits would be derived by expanding the storage capacity to 15 million barrels?   To 20 million barrels?

9-5. Now consider an infinite-time horizon for the petroleum company.   Inventories on hand at the end of each winter season are no longer credited at the arbitrary rate of $3 a barrel, but instead are carried forward into the following summer.   You may suppose that the costs and probability distributions remain stationary over the indefinite future.

Write down the linear programming formulation for the 10-million-barrel storage situation.   If you are really ambitious, try to find the optimal solution.

CHAPTER TEN

COST AND VALUE
OF INFORMATION

Introduction

All along in this volume, the reader has witnessed the introduction of progressively more powerful tools of analysis and a corresponding extension of the range within which business decisions can be treated by rational analysis in place of purely intuitive judgments. First came two-dimensional and then multi-dimensional product-mix problems, then downward-sloping instead of constant marginal revenue curves, then integer programming to analyze economies of scale and also batch sequencing, then static and finally sequential inventory problems involving the use of probabilities in place of best estimates.

With each step in the expansion of the radius of knowledge, there has been a more than proportional increase in the area bordering upon the unknown. Each step should have made the reader keenly aware of how difficult it is to set up a tidy and rational idealization of the real world of business decision and, at the same time, how misleading it can be to rely solely upon intuitive solutions to complex decision problems. This book will have served its purpose if only it has induced the reader to become a little less dogmatic about the role of human intuition. There are substantial advantages in combining intuition with logic—

above all, in employing intuition to isolate the essential features of the infinitely complex real world, the features that really need to be considered within a sensible model of reality. In no small measure, the art of model building consists in recognizing the importance of neglecting the negligible and of ignoring those factors which are truly irrelevant to the decision at hand.

In this final chapter, in which we are concerned with actions on the basis of small amounts of information, the link between intuition and logic becomes essential. Following the "personalistic" school of thought among statisticians, we shall adopt the viewpoint that, in order to translate prior experience into a plan of action, it is desirable to make use of personal probabilities.[1] These personal probabilities are inherently subjective and vary from one individual to the next, depending upon the man's experiences and also upon his prejudices.

This chapter contains two illustrations of the use of personal probabilities to evaluate present versus future information. One of these examples involves a single decision and deals with the development of a new product. The other is a sequential planning problem, one in which there are several alternations between decisions and the receipt of new information. In both examples the timing of information is an essential element in the decision-making process.

One vital feature is still missing. No attempt has been made to take account of the uncertainty that results from unpredictability of responses to the firm's actions by other purposeful entities, e.g. competitors, labor unions, and regulatory commissions. These considerations belong more properly under the heading of game theory.[2]

Development of a new product

The Titanic Chemical Corporation has developed a new plastic but is unsure which of two alternative production methods will

[1] See L. J. Savage, *The Foundations of Statistics*, John Wiley & Sons, Inc., New York, 1954. Also R. Schlaiffer, *Probability and Statistics for Business Decisions*, McGraw-Hill Book Company, Inc., New York, 1959.

[2] See M. Shubik, *Strategy and Market Structure*, John Wiley & Sons, Inc., New York, 1959.

turn out to be less expensive: a high-pressure or a low-pressure process. Four alternative decisions are to be compared: (*a*) proceed immediately with the construction of a high-pressure plant; (*b*) proceed immediately with the construction of a low-pressure plant; (*c*) flip a fair coin to decide which one to build; or (*d*) delay construction until after obtaining reliable information from pilot-plant experiments. Phrased in this way, this amounts to a nonsequential decision problem—much more closely akin to the single-period rather than the multi-period inventory models of the preceding chapter.

In case of proceeding immediately and selecting the incorrect process, future modification costs are likely to be high—in the neighborhood of $5 million. The costs of delay are also high and quite debatable in magnitude—anywhere between $1 and $5

TABLE 10-1. COSTS OF ALTERNATIVE DECISIONS AND OCCURRENCES
(Millions of dollars)

Alternative actions \ Alternative occurrences	Probability of occurrence	High-pressure process turns out to be more successful	Low-pressure process turns out to be more successful	Expected costs
		p	$(1-p)$	
(*a*) Construct high-pressure plant immediately........		0	5	$5(1-p)$
(*b*) Construct low-pressure plant immediately........		5	0	$5p$
(*c*) Flip a fair coin...........		$(\frac{1}{2})(5)$	$(\frac{1}{2})(5)$	2.5
(*d*) Delay construction.......		D	D	D

million. A delay will involve the loss of potential profits during one or two years of pilot-plant work, plus further losses due to the possibility that a competitor may get entrenched in the market meanwhile. The costs associated with the various alternatives are summarized in Table 10-1, using the symbols D and p to represent the more conjectural elements of the problem—respectively, the costs of delay and the probability that the high-pressure process will turn out to be the preferable one.

On the basis of Table 10-1, it is possible to arrive at one preliminary conclusion concerning actions (c) and (d) alone: If D, the costs of delay, are greater than \$2.5 million, it is better to flip a coin and proceed immediately rather than to delay! Flipping a coin means that the company runs a 50-50 chance of incurring costs of \$5 million, i.e., expected costs of only \$2.5 million. This conclusion holds true regardless of the numerical values attached to the probabilities p and $(1 - p)$.

Figure 10-1 contains a plot of the two most conjectural parameters D and p and establishes the zones within which each of the

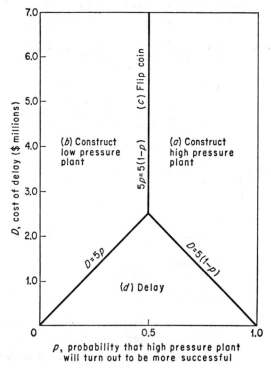

Fig. 10-1. Optimal actions for alternative costs of delay and probabilities of success.

alternative actions is best. The diagram does not show us directly what action to take, but it does appreciably narrow down the alternatives. Several common-sense results appear: (1) The lower the cost of delay, the more advantageous becomes a delay. (2) The greater the company's uncertainty as to which process is best, the more closely p approaches the indifference value of .5 and the more desirable becomes a delay.[1] (3) Flipping a coin is justifiable only when the two processes are considered equally likely to be good *and* when the costs of delay exceed $2.5 million.

Bayes' theorem

Essential to the understanding of sequential decision problems is Bayes' theorem. This is a theorem that tells us how to combine newly acquired sample information with prior personal probabilities to come up with revised personal probabilities. Using these revised personal probabilities, a new course of action can be taken, more information acquired, personal probabilities revised again, and so on.

First we shall give a numerical example and then the theorem. In Chapter 9, the Delphic Computing Company was described as being certain of the probability distribution of demand during each year: a $\frac{2}{3}$ probability of zero and a $\frac{1}{3}$ probability of one unit. Suppose instead that the company holds several competing hypotheses and is uncertain which of the alternatives is correct. In Table 10-2, the symbol $p(z|H)$ is used to denote the probability of a specified demand z, given that the hypothesis H holds true. The table says, for example, that, if A holds true, there is a $\frac{5}{6}$ chance that the demand will be zero; but if B is true, there is just a $\frac{5}{12}$ chance of zero. This illustration is constructed for the easy case of two competing hypotheses, A and B, but it could just as well be extended to deal with tens or hundreds of such alternatives.

Now, *if* the decision maker is willing to take the further step of

---

[1] What would be the indifference value of p if the penalties for incorrect action were no longer symmetrical, e.g., if the cost of modification from a low- to a high-pressure plant rose to $10 million?

TABLE 10-2. CONDITIONAL PROBABILITIES OF DEMAND UNDER TWO COMPETING HYPOTHESES

Probability of demand for	Hypothesis A	Hypothesis B
Zero units................	$p(0\|A) = \frac{5}{6}$	$p(0\|B) = \frac{5}{12}$
One unit.................	$p(1\|A) = \frac{1}{6}$	$p(1\|B) = \frac{7}{12}$

attaching his own personal probabilities to the competing hypotheses, he will be in a position to start making recommendations on inventory policy. For example, if he believes that hypothesis A is a little more likely to be true than hypothesis B, this might be

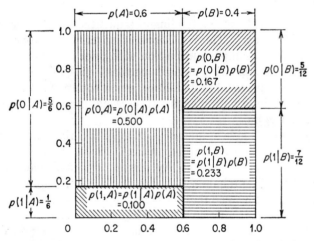

Fig. 10-2. Joint probabilities for specific demands and hypotheses.

interpreted quantitatively to mean that he ascribes a personal probability of .6 to A and .4 to B.* From these personal probabilities *and* from the conditional probabilities listed in Table 10-2, we can derive the joint probabilities shown in Figure 10-2.

* Much of the criticism of Bayes' theorem has been aimed at something quite different: the fallacy of equal probability of the unknown. Given n competing hypotheses, there is no reason to insist that the decision maker always attach a personal probability of $1/n$ to each of the alternative possibilities.

Along the horizontal scale on this figure are plotted the subjective probabilities, $p(A)$ and $p(B)$, for the two competing hypotheses, A and B. The vertical scale is marked off in proportion to the conditional probabilities $p(z|H)$. Through this construction, the *areas* of the four rectangles are proportional to the joint probability $p(z,H)$ that demand z will occur *and* that hypothesis H is true. For example, if z represents a demand for zero units and if H represents hypothesis A:

Joint probability of both a demand for z units
    and hypothesis H being true

$$\begin{aligned} &= p(z,H) \\ &= p(0,A) \\ &= p(0|A)p(A) \\ &= (\tfrac{5}{6})(.6) \\ &= .500 \end{aligned}$$

Since either A is true or else B is true, this diagram also permits us to calculate the unconditional probability of finding that the demand is zero. This particular example was set up so as to lead to the same *un*conditional probabilities of demand as in the previous chapter's illustration. For example,

Unconditional probability
    of a zero demand

$$\begin{aligned} &= p(0) \\ &= p(0|A)p(A) + p(0|B)p(B) \quad \text{(10-1)} \\ &= .500 + .167 \\ &= .667 \end{aligned}$$

What if now we were to observe a year in which the demand actually turned out to be zero? How would this new piece of information lead to a revision of the initial subjective probabilities? Since zero is much more likely to occur under hypothesis A than under hypothesis B, it is plausible that the credibility of hypothesis A should be increased as a result of the observation. But how much of an increase should be associated with this single observation? Common sense suggests a figure of $.500/.667 = .750$ as the new value for the probability of A, given that a zero demand has been observed. This new value can be denoted by the symbol $p(A|0)$ and, in general, by $p(H|z)$. Common sense can be reinforced by the following proof:

Joint probability of both a demand for z units and hypothesis H being true
$$= p(z,H)$$
$$= p(z|H)p(H) = p(H|z)p(z)$$

Therefore, probability of H being true, given an observed demand of z units
$$= p(H|z) = \frac{p(z|H)p(H)}{p(z)} \quad (10\text{-}2)$$

Equation (10-2) is known as Bayes' theorem. This relationship provides a systematic method for revising initial probabilities in the light of new data. For example, after the single observation of a zero demand,

$$p(A|0) = \frac{p(0|A)p(A)}{p(0)} = \frac{.500}{.667} = .75 \quad (10\text{-}3)$$

Now suppose that we obtained a second observation of a zero demand. Using the revised personal probabilities $p(H|0)$ and applying Bayes' theorem once more,

Probability of A being true, given two successive observations of a zero demand
$$= p(A|0,0) = \frac{p(0|A)p(A|0)}{p(0,0)}$$
$$= \frac{p(0|A)p(A|0)}{p(0|A)p(A|0) + p(0|B)p(B|0)}$$
$$= \frac{(\tfrac{5}{6})(.75)}{(\tfrac{5}{6})(.75) + (\tfrac{5}{12})(.25)} = .86$$

Bayes' theorem seldom enables us to become absolutely sure that any given hypothesis is either true or false. (Absolute certainty of a hypothesis is produced in the event that a given series of observations is consistent with only that one conceivable hypothesis.) The theorem does guarantee, however, that, as the sample size increases, our confidence in one or the other alternative is almost certain to approach unity. For example:

Initial personal probability of A $\qquad = p(A) = .60$

Personal probability of A after one demand of
zero $\qquad\qquad\qquad\qquad\qquad\qquad\qquad = p(A|0) = .75$

Personal probability of A after two demands
of zero $\qquad\qquad\qquad\qquad\qquad\qquad\quad = p(A|0,0) = .86$

In contrast with more conventional statistical methods for estimation and hypothesis testing, the personalistic approach permits the analyst to draw inferences and to recommend actions on the basis of extremely small samples. The personalistic viewpoint is oriented toward normative rather than purely descriptive models of behavior. This approach is an appealing one for the analysis of business decisions in which, unlike the physical sciences, it is almost never feasible to marshal a sizable sample of directly relevant evidence. Yet, there is no magic in the personalistic approach. Small-sample inferences and actions are strongly influenced by the initial values chosen for the personal probabilities, that is to say, by the good judgment and the intuition of the analyst himself. Moreover, the tidiness of this approach is a result of the supposition that the only competing hypotheses are those known *prior* to examining the sample data. We are not permitted to use sample evidence twice—once for suggesting preliminary hypotheses and then a second time for purposes of statistical estimation.

Application to inventory control

In most cases, in order to make use of these ideas for purposes of sequential inventory control, the state variable is given at least one additional dimension. To specify the state of the system at any given point in time, it is necessary to know not only the current level of inventory but also something about previous levels of demand.

For purposes of illustration, let us work with the two-period finite-horizon model of the Delphic Computer Company (refer back to Figure 9-4). The identical ordering costs, shortage costs, and discount factor will be employed as in the previous chapter. The only difference is that we are going to use Bayes' theorem and take the first period's decision in light of the fact that we are going to acquire more precise knowledge of the demand pattern prior to making a decision for the second period.

It will be assumed that the conditional probabilities of demand are those appearing in Table 10-2 and that the initial values for the personal probabilities are again $p(A) = .6$ and $p(B) = .4$. Bayes' theorem has already been used to revise these initial probabilities for the case in which the initial demand turned out to be zero. Through similar calculations, the reader may verify the balance of Table 10-3.

TABLE 10-3

Initial observation	Revised personal probabilities, given observation z [see Eq. (10-2)]		Revised probabilities of demand, given observation z [see Eq. (10-1)]	
	$p(A\|z)$	$p(B\|z)$	$p(0\|z) = p(0\|A)p(A\|z) + p(0\|B)p(B\|z)$	$p(1\|z) = p(1\|A)p(A\|z) + p(1\|B)p(B\|z)$
$z = 0$	.75	.25	$\frac{35}{48}$	$\frac{13}{48}$
$z = 1$	.30	.70	$\frac{26}{48}$	$\frac{22}{48}$

Utilizing the information of Table 10-3, a flow diagram may be constructed for the company's sequential structure of information and of action. (Figure 10-3, a flow diagram for the *sequential* decision case, is completely analogous to Table 10-1, the costs of alternative decisions and occurrences in the *single* decision model of the Titanic Chemical Company's new plastic development.) The decision maker starts at position A in the flow diagram and then moves to position B, C, or D, depending upon the number of spare drums specified by his initial order: 2, 1, or 0. Also as before, his final situation will be either L, M, or N, with no salvage credits assigned to ending inventory. The only difference from the non-Bayes model is that, instead of defining the second period's position in terms of inventory alone, the decision

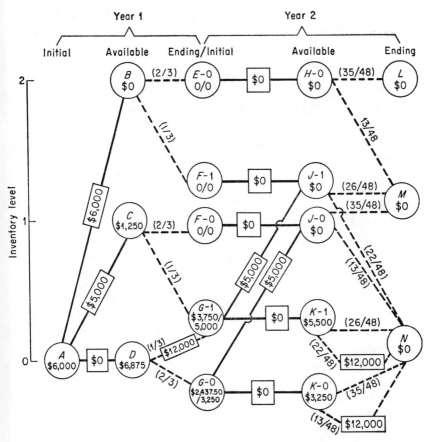

Fig. 10-3. Bayes version of the Delphic inventory problem.

maker must also specify the previous demand. In Figure 9-4, for example, it made no difference which of three possible paths resulted in position G (a second-year initial inventory of zero): a first-year order for one unit followed by a demand for one; an order for zero followed by a demand for one; or an order for zero followed by a demand for zero.

In Figure 10-3, a distinction is essential. Here there are two states for which the second period's initial inventory is zero:

G-0 corresponding to a previous demand of zero, and G-1 to a previous demand of one. According to Table 10-3, at availability levels connected with G-1, the probability of a demand for one unit during the second period is $22\frac{2}{48}$—almost twice the probability of $13\frac{3}{48}$ associated with positions connected to G-0 and a previous demand of zero. As a result of this difference in probabilities, it turns out that the non-Bayes optimal strategy is no longer fully applicable.

In order to carry out the evaluation procedure, we begin at the terminal states L, M, and N and proceed recursively. At inventory availability levels of H-0, J-1, and J-0, there is no possibility of a shortage; therefore, the cost valuation of these positions is zero. At K-1 and K-0, shortages are possible. With costs of \$12,000 per shortage and with expected shortages of $22\frac{2}{48}$ at position K-1, future costs are valued at \$5,500 in that position. But at K-0 with expected shortages of $13\frac{3}{48}$, these costs are only \$3,250. Accordingly, there is a big difference between positions G-1 and G-0 in the relative attractiveness of incurring a \$5,000 cost for ordering a spare unit. At G-1, it is cheaper to incur this ordering cost than to run the risk of a shortage; but at G-0, the reverse is true. In the non-Bayes case of Figure 9-4, it never paid to order at the beginning of period 2. In this case, because of the changed estimate of the probability distribution, it is worthwhile to order provided that the initial inventory is zero and that there was a demand during the first time period.

The two different ordering policies result in a cost of \$5,000 and \$3,250, respectively, for the second-period positions G-1 and G-0. Discounting these costs by the present-worth factor of .75, we convert them into first-period costs of \$3,750 and \$2,437.50. The schedule of ending inventory values for the first period, together with the shortage costs and the demand probabilities, leads to the price tags placed on positions B, C, and D. [Reviewing equation (10-1), we remind ourselves that the first period's demand probabilities are identical with those in the non-Bayes formulation: a $\frac{2}{3}$ probability of zero and a $\frac{1}{3}$ probability of one unit.]

Finally, from positions B, C, and D, we arrive back at the decision maker's starting point, A. From A, the least expensive course of action is to order two units, incur an immediate cost of $6,000, and move to B with subsequent costs of zero. Unlike the illustration for the non-Bayes case, this is a cheaper course of action than ordering a single unit. Note that, as a result of introducing personal probabilities and applying Bayes' rule, one action leads to unchanged costs, an order for two units; but that an order for a single unit results in an *in*crease in costs from $6,000 to $6,250; and that a zero order leads to a *de*crease from $7,000 to $6,875.

A non-Bayes solution may yield a reasonable first approximation in cases of decision making under uncertainty. The Bayes formulation does, however, approach more closely what the practical man has in mind when he says, "Let's cross that bridge when we come to it." A Bayes model points toward understanding what is involved in the typical long-range business decision: one in which there is an immediate cost attached to gaining future flexibility. This does not imply that all difficult decisions should be put off until tomorrow—only those for which the expected benefits outweigh the costs of delay.

EXERCISES

10-1. Diana Detergents Corporation is attempting to develop a new product for use in regions where the water is especially hard. If successful in obtaining such a product before its competitors do so, the firm stands to gain $10 million in profits.

A number of alternative research and development projects appear equally likely to succeed—each with probability p and with equal expected costs, $500,000 apiece. Under alternative assumptions about the probability of success for an individual project, how many different projects is it worthwhile for the company to support simultaneously?[1]

10-2. In view of recent channel improvements, the Acheron Barge Line is planning to acquire some new equipment. Three

[1] Adapted from formulation by Richard Nelson.

forecasters have been asked to present their views: Ed, Henry, and Sandy. Each is a sophisticated statistician and puts his prediction in the form of a probability distribution. For example, Ed's forecast is to be read as follows: In 4 out of 10 years, traffic will increase by 300 thousand tons; in 6 out of 10 years, by 400 thousand tons; there is no chance that the growth will ever be as much as 500 thousand tons.

Probability of increase of	Ed's forecast	Henry's forecast	Sandy's forecast
300 thousand tons.........	.4	.2	.1
400 thousand tons.........	.6	.5	.4
500 thousand tons.........	0	.3	.5

On the basis of previous experience, the directors of the line have voted to attach a 30 per cent probability to Ed's prediction, 40 per cent to Henry's, and 30 per cent to Sandy's. How would these initial probabilities be revised if the first year's growth turned out to be 400 thousand tons? If the second year's growth were 500 thousand? What would be the corresponding probabilities for traffic growth during each of the three years?

10-3. Reconstruct Figure 10-3, inserting salvage credits of $300 for each computer drum on hand at the end of the second year. Compare these results with those of exercise 9-2.

10-4. Reconstruct Figure 10-3 for the case of a three-year instead of a two-year cutoff date. Also, by analogy with equation (9-1), write down the corresponding functional equation. You may neglect salvage credits, and you may assume that the company's demand experience can always be summarized in terms of the *sum* of past demands.[1] The inventory level is not to exceed two units at any time.

[1] For a statement of conditions under which the sum is a "sufficient statistic," see H. Scarf, "Bayes Solutions of the Statistical Inventory Problem," *Annals of Mathematical Statistics*, June, 1959.

BIBLIOGRAPHY

The following represents just a small fraction of the published material related to the topics included within this volume. For a well-organized and highly comprehensive bibliography containing over 1,000 items, see V. Riley and S. I. Gass, *Linear Programming and Associated Techniques*, Johns Hopkins Press, Baltimore, 1958.

General economics; the logic of choice; oligopoly

Dean, J., *Managerial Economics*, Prentice-Hall, Inc., Englewood Cliffs, N.J., 1951.
> An introductory text. Covers competition, multiple products, demand analysis, cost concepts, advertising, pricing, and capital budgeting.

Duesenberry, J. S., and T. E. Preston, *Cases and Problems in Economics*, Prentice-Hall, Inc., Englewood Cliffs, N.J., 1960.
> Particularly useful in reviewing basic concepts through concrete applications.

Grant, E. L., and W. G. Ireson, *Principles of Engineering Economy*, 4th ed., The Ronald Press Company, New York, 1960.
> Analysis of investment in capital goods. Covers time discounting; depreciation accounting; income tax considerations; incremental and sunk costs; dynamic equipment replacement policy.

McKean, R. N., *Efficiency in Government through Systems Analysis*, John Wiley & Sons, Inc., New York, 1958.

Special emphasis on the logic of water resources development. Alternative investment criteria; discounting of costs and benefits; suboptimization.

Samuelson, P. A., *Economics: An Introductory Analysis*, 5th ed., McGraw-Hill Book Company, Inc., New York, 1961.

An introductory text. National income; money and banking; business cycles; composition and pricing of national output; distribution of income; international trade and finance.

Shubik, M., *Strategy and Market Structure*, John Wiley & Sons, Inc., New York, 1959.

Competition, oligopoly, and the theory of games.

General references on operations research

Bowman, E. H., and R. B. Fetter, *Analysis for Production Management*, Richard D. Irwin, Inc., Homewood, Ill., rev. ed., 1961.

An introductory text with special emphasis on industrial engineering applications. Includes both linear programming and statistical analysis.

Bowman, E. H., and R. B. Fetter (eds.), *Analyses of Industrial Operations*, Richard D. Irwin, Inc., Homewood, Ill., 1959.

An anthology of empirical studies. Includes applications of linear programming, inventory control, queuing theory, and incremental analysis.

Churchman, C. W., R. L. Ackoff, and E. L. Arnoff, *Introduction to Operations Research*, John Wiley & Sons, Inc., New York, 1957.

One of the more all-inclusive volumes in this area. Special stress on the implementation of studies within the business firm. A valuable source of reference material.

Linear programming

Charnes, A., W. W. Cooper, and B. Mellon, "Blending Aviation Gasolines: A Study in Programming Interdependent Activities in an Integrated Oil Company," *Econometrica*, April, 1952.

One of the earliest practical applications of linear programming. Has directly stimulated a large amount of work within the petroleum and chemical industries.

Dantzig, G. B., and P. Wolfe, "The Decomposition Algorithm for Linear Programs," *Econometrica*, October, 1961.

A technique for splitting up certain types of large linear programs into smaller and more manageable subproblems. Besides holding promise for the efficient computation of large-scale systems, the principle yields a certain rationale for internal prices and decentralized decision making within the firm.

Dorfman, R., P. A. Samuelson, and R. M. Solow, *Linear Programming and Economic Analysis*, McGraw-Hill Book Company, Inc., New York, 1958.

An authoritative treatment of the relationships between linear programming, the traditional theory of competitive economic equilibrium, the Von Neumann model of capital accumulation, and the theory of games.

Gass, S. I., *Linear Programming*, McGraw-Hill Book Company, Inc., New York, 1958.

One of the best available books on linear programming computational methods. Introduces the reader to matrix algebra; compares the original and the revised simplex methods; discusses duality, degeneracy, and parametric linear programming.

Heady, E. O., and W. Candler, *Linear Programming Methods*, Iowa State College Press, Ames, Iowa, 1958.

Especially useful for agricultural examples.

Koopmans, T. C. (ed.), *Activity Analysis of Production and Allocation*, John Wiley & Sons, Inc., New York, 1951.

Contains the classical papers on linear programming: Dantzig on the simplex method; Koopmans on production as an efficient allocation of activities; and Koopmans and Reiter on the transportation model.

Massé, P., and R. Gibrat, "Application of Linear Programming to Investments in the Electric Power Industry," *Management Science*, January, 1957.[1]

An ingenious application in a case involving joint products: peak and off-peak electric power.

Orchard-Hays, W., "Evolution of Linear Programming Computing Techniques," *Management Science*, January, 1958.

A history of the development of electronic computing techniques; written by one of the pioneers in these techniques.

Vajda, S., *Readings in Linear Programming*, John Wiley & Sons, Inc., New York, 1958.

A concise description of a variety of applications: the transportation problem, production scheduling, bid evaluation, routing aircraft, gasoline blending, and trim loss reduction.

---

[1] Also reprinted in Bowman and Fetter (eds.), *Analyses of Industrial Operations*.

Inventory models; dynamic programming

Arrow, K. J., S. Karlin, and H. Scarf (eds.), *Studies in the Mathematical Theory of Inventory and Production*, Stanford University Press, Stanford, 1958.

General mathematical concepts behind efficient inventory and production control.

Bellman, R., *Dynamic Programming*, Princeton University Press, Princeton, N.J., 1957.

A synthesis of the author's contributions to the mathematical theory of sequential decision processes.

Brown, R. G., *Statistical Forecasting for Inventory Control*, McGraw-Hill Book Company, Inc., New York, 1959.

Stresses practical methods for the extrapolation of demand experience.

d'Epenoux, F., "Sur un Problème de production et de stockage dans l'aléatoire," *Revue française de recherche opérationnelle*, no. 14, 1960.

Shows how to convert an infinite-horizon dynamic programming model into a linear programming format. Describes relationship to Markov chain optimization.

Holt, C. C., F. Modigliani, and H. A. Simon, "A Linear Decision Rule for Production and Employment Scheduling," *Management Science*, October, 1955. Also, C. C. Holt, F. Modigliani, and J. F. Muth, "Derivation of a Linear Decision Rule for Production and Employment," *Management Science*, January, 1956.[1]

These two papers describe a special case of inventory and production control—quadratic cost functions—in which it is justifiable to insert expected values of demand in place of probability distributions.

Little, J. D. C., "The Use of Storage Water in a Hydroelectric System," *Journal of the Operations Research Society of America*, May, 1955.

Analysis of water storage by dynamic programming.

Magee, J. F., *Production Planning and Inventory Control*, McGraw-Hill Book Company, Inc., New York, 1958.

Emphasizes practical methods for the implementation of control systems.

Scarf, H., "The Optimality of *S, s* Policies in the Dynamic Inventory Problem," in K. Arrow, S. Karlin, and P. Suppes (eds.), *Mathematical Methods in the Social Sciences*, 1959, Stanford University Press, Stanford, 1960.

[1] Also reprinted in Bowman and Fetter (eds.), *Analyses of Industrial Operations*.

Conditions under which it is optimal to pursue a simple reorder point policy.

Probabilistic allocation models

Ferguson, A. R., and G. B. Dantzig, "The Allocation of Aircraft to Routes," *Management Science*, October, 1956.[1]
   An example of linear programming under uncertain demand.
Freund, R. J., "The Introduction of Risk into a Programming Model," *Econometrica*, July, 1956.
   Employs a quadratic programming model in order to deal with risk aversion. Based upon a crop-combination example.
Markowitz, H. M., *Portfolio Selection*, John Wiley & Sons, Inc., New York, 1959.
   Presents a theory of efficient diversification of investments. Utilizes quadratic programming to analyze the trade-offs between variance and mean return on a portfolio.

Queuing theory; simulation

Feller, W., *An Introduction to Probability Theory and Its Applications*, vol. 1, 2d ed., John Wiley & Sons, Inc., New York, 1957.
   Chapter 17 includes a discussion of the theory of waiting lines and of servicing problems.
Heller, J., "Some Numerical Experiments for an $M \times J$ Flow Shop and Its Decision-theoretical Aspects," *Operations Research*, March–April, 1960.
   A numerical experiment with a job sequencing problem. Observes that, if priorities are randomly assigned and if a large sample of alternative schedules is drawn, the make-span will be approximately normally distributed.
Malcolm, D. G., "Bibliography on the Use of Simulation in Management Analysis," *Operations Research*, March–April, 1960.
   A bibliography containing over 150 items in the area of computer simulation, military gaming, and management gaming.
Mangelsdorf, T. M., "Waiting Line Theory Applied to Manufacturing Problems," in Bowman and Fetter (eds.), *Analyses of Industrial Operations*.
   Deals with the practical implementation of queuing models.

[1] Also reprinted in Bowman and Fetter (eds.), *Analyses of Industrial Operations*.

Sasieni, M., A. Yaspan, and L. Friedman, *Operations Research,* John Wiley & Sons, Inc., New York, 1959.

    A highly readable introduction to queuing theory and to Monte Carlo methods can be found in Chapter 6.

Cost and value of information; organization theory

Beckmann, M., "Decision and Team Problems in Airline Reservations," *Econometrica,* January, 1958.

    An empirical application of decision making and communication in teams. Deals with the costs and benefits of centralized versus decentralized organizations.

Bennion, E. G., "Capital Budgeting and Game Theory," *Harvard Business Review,* November–December, 1956.

    An introduction to the problem of decision making under uncertainty. Emphasizes the concept of indifference probabilities.

Marschak, J., "Towards an Economic Theory of Information and Organization," in R. M. Thrall, C. H. Coombs, and R. L. Davis (eds.), *Decision Processes,* John Wiley & Sons, Inc., New York, 1954.

    A theory of the rational firm in the domain of uncertainty. Special emphasis upon the character of the firm as a team.

Marschak, J., "Remarks on the Economics of Information," in *Contributions to Scientific Research in Management,* University of California Press, Berkeley, Calif., 1960.

    Distinguishes between economic value of information and entropy as a physical measure of information.

Radner, R., "The Application of Linear Programming to Team Decision Problems," *Management Science,* January, 1959.

    Compares optimal decision rules within centralized and decentralized organizations.

Savage, L. J., *The Foundations of Statistics,* John Wiley & Sons, Inc., New York, 1954.

    An axiomatization of the personalistic viewpoint in statistics. Views statistics as the discipline of rational decision in the face of uncertainty.

Schlaifer, R., *Probability and Statistics for Business Decisions,* McGraw-Hill Book Company, Inc., New York, 1959.

    Applies the personalistic viewpoint to business decisions. Concentrates upon sampling, quality control, and inventory control.

INDEX

Ackoff, R. L., 170
Activity, definition of, 30
Arnoff, E. L., 170
Arrow, K., 141n., 147n., 172
Artificial variable, definition of, 37
Avi-Itzhak, B., 133n.

Baker, C. J., 110n.
Basic feasible solution, definition
    of, 29
Basing-point system, 81–83, 91, 92
Basis, definition of, 29, 30
Basis theorem, 31
Bayes' theorem, 159–163
Beckmann, M., 95n., 174
Bellman, R., 136n., 140n., 147n.,
    172
Bennion, E. G., 174
Bishop, C. E., 44n.
Bowman, E. H., 170–173
Brown, R. G., 172

Candler, W., 171
Capacity expansion, 103–106

Capital budgeting, 6–8
Charnes, A., 71, 72, 170
Churchman, C. W., 170
Congruence, 99, 100
Coombs, C. H., 174
Cooper, W. W., 170
Cost data, estimation of, 9, 47, 48,
    64, 65, 121, 122
Cutoff rate of return, 7, 8
Cutting plane for integer program-
    ming, 99–103

Dantzig, G. B., 4n., 72n., 91n.,
    170, 171, 173
Davis, R. L., 174
Dean, J., 169
Degeneracy, 34, 71–74
Demand curves, inclusion within
    linear programming models,
    86, 87
Discounted cash flow, 104, 106
Dorfman, R., 171
Dual variables (see Implicit prices)
Duesenberry, J. S., 169